Such Tender Years

The admission and treatment of
youngsters aged 14 and under,
with learning difficulties or mental illness
to the three asylums in Leicestershire – between
1836 to 1912

Taken from the records of the Superintendents,
Medical Officers and Official Visitors

Collated by Di Lockley

Such tender years

Cover designed by Patrick Lockley

ISBN: 978-1-907540-82-0

Published January 2013

Printed and Published by Anchorprint Group Limited
www.anchorprint.co.uk

Acknowledgements

Acknowledgement is given to all who have assisted in the preparation of this publication:–

My thanks firstly go to Peter Birkett the former Hospital Manager at the 2nd County Asylum sited in Narborough. He took exceptional care of both the 1st and 2nd County Asylum records until they were ultimately taken to the Record Office of Leicestershire, Leicester and Rutland in South Wigston. Without his care this research would not be in existence.

I will always be indebted to the staff at the Record Office who continually had to go to the back room to collect my document requests, with the case books themselves being very heavy and cumbersome. My thanks must more specifically go to Adam Goodwin who was in charge of collecting and collating all the records and getting them ready for Record Office access, for the general public. He also gives continuing support and advice.

My gratitude also going to Alex Cave the University of Leicester Archivist who carefully selected any illustrative records that are still held within the University Records and were useful for both of my publications.

I cannot show appreciation enough to Fiona Moir (a retired Leicestershire Head Teacher for children with special needs). She gave so much time to the much needed editing of this publication. Her expert advice was much appreciated.

My husband Tony was my photographer of records at the Record Office and he also spent many hours completing the superb drawing of the Borough Asylum and the 2nd County Asylum, plus other maps and plans.

My younger son Patrick, with his artistic genius, once again designed the outside cover of the book.

My thanks must also go to Richard Linnett at Anchor Print whose assistance and publishing services have always been outstanding.

'Confinement, probation or punishment of any inmate' was forbidden without medical authority. There was to be 'no deceit or terrifying of patients, or irritation by mockery or mimicry'. The keepers 'shall not indulge or express vindictive feelings'; they were to 'forgive all petulance on the part of the patients and treat with equal tenderness those who give the least trouble'.

1st County Asylum Regulations 1837

Preface

I am a retired teacher. At the start of my career I was employed teaching primary children of normal ability but subsequently was trained to teach children with learning difficulties both moderate and severe.

The duration of my research with the County asylum records has lasted many years. The intent of my first publication 'The House of Cure' was to increase awareness of the formidable 1st County Asylum records still extant in the Leicestershire, Leicester and Rutland Record Office. Other professionals and any predecessors of former asylum patients were also given information on what they could expect to find within various ancient ledgers. It was also imperative to emphasize what a forward thinking and progressive institution this particular asylum was. Fifty percent of over seven thousand admissions returned cured or much relieved to their former lifestyles.

I am avid historian and I initially discovered the asylum records when trying to find out what happened to the children with more severe learning difficulties almost a century ago. It was always my intention to go back to the younger patients and view their records in much greater detail.

'Such tender years' is primarily intended for other professionals who have also have experience of working either with children who have learning difficulties or children who are mentally ill. For this research the records from three asylums (1st County, 2nd County and the Borough) have all been referred to

This publication encompasses the treatment of any admission of a patient aged fourteen and under at the time of admission, whose medical records or reception order certificates are still available for reference at the Record Office in South Wigston, Leicestershire.

Glossary of terms used within this publication

Dementia – Decay or obliteration of the intellectual faculties

Erysipelas – Contagious skin disease due to streptococci and bulbous legions

Feeble minded – Obsolete term for mental retardation and learning difficulty.

Friends – Term occasionally used for the adults most closely linked to a patient, which appeared at times to be their closest relatives.

General paralysis of the insane – GPI – A syndrome of weakness and madness occurring in tertiary syphilis

Hysteria – A real disease with physical symptoms which cannot be attributed to any underlying physical causes

Idiot – Obsolete term for a person of very low intelligence, whose intellectual faculties have never been developed, having a mental age of less than 3 years old

Imbecile – Obsolete term for a person of the second order of mental retardation, above the level of idiocy, having a mental age of seven or eight years

Insanity – A term for any form of mental illness, which renders a person incapable of acting in accordance with the legal and conventional standards of the times.

Lunacy and Lunatic – Obsolete term for a mentally ill person originally derived from a supposed connection between mental illness and the moon

Melancholia – A mental condition characterised by great depression of spirits and gloomy foreboding

Mania – A type of effective disorder characterised by euphoric mood, excessive activity and talkativeness, impaired judgement, affecting all the operations of the brain

Phthisis – Chronic wasting away or another name for tuberculosis

Relieving Officer – RO – The local medical officer, most commonly a general practitioner too, who was responsible for organising the admission of patient in his area to an asylum.

Settlement area – This was the area where a patient's treatment was chargeable to. It was usually where they had been born for these young patients.

Status epilepticus – Is a life–threatening condition in which the brain is in a state of persistent seizure.

Union Workhouse – When a workhouse is termed as a Union Workhouse, it is when a group of parishes have got together to provide one.

Contents

Introduction

Thomas [1]

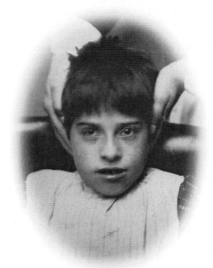

Mabel

John William [4]

Mary Beryl

Such youthful faces – Such *tender years.* These are photographs of just six youngsters that were not taken at home or in the abodes of relatives. In fact their actual parents may never have seen these images. All these pictures were taken as part of the later admissions to one of the three Leicestershire Lunatic Asylums of yesteryear, once photographic apparatus had been purchased in 1897 at the 1st County Asylum and in 1900 at the Borough Asylum at Humberstone. The youth of the patient is at times emphasized by the requirement for them to stand on a chair. The 2nd County Asylum opened at Narborough after the 1st sited at the University closed in 1908. There were almost two hundred admissions of patients aged fourteen years and under to these 3 asylums in Leicestershire.

Duncan

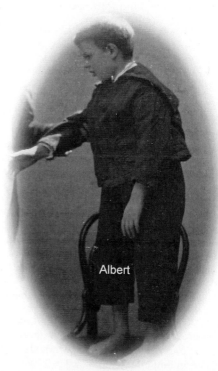

Albert

Leicestershire's young asylum patients were from families who were living and working during the Nineteenth century, an era of quite dramatic, innovative changes. A predominantly rural county with its large herds of sheep and cattle helped supply the raw materials, which aided the development of stocking and shoe making. These workers from one of the market towns or innumerable villages had most commonly been industrious within family workshops, either within the dwelling itself or in an outhouse adjoining the homestead.

Radical developments within the Leicestershire transport system fired ground-breaking industrial progress. New canal and rail networks enabled the quicker transportation of goods of which coal from the mines in the north west was one of the most lucrative. Sarah Susan Ravina's stepfather was mining coal in Ellistown. The extensive rocky outcrops also in the more northerly section were set to be quarried and surface town and city streets both locally and hundreds of miles distant.

Leicester's population figures were rising at formidable rates from 17,000 in 1801 to 211,600 in 1901. The housing within the market towns and particularly Leicester's streets were growing rapidly out into the more rural suburbs. Many of the families were living in an abode sited amongst rows of terraced houses, which were interspersed by the new factories. John Samuel Clifford's father John was a warehouseman in the shoe trade in the 1901 Census.

Eventually, the more cottage based industries, moved towards production lines within the market towns, with light engineering being born too. All these innovations did not necessarily result in reasonable family living standards for all. The majority of framework knitters, for example had hired their machines and eventually due to factory production lines were left with no work orders, but rent for their frames was still due to be paid.

Many fathers trying to find a livelihood to sustain reasonable family lifestyles were working away from their families in such occupations as general labouring, quarrying, excavating canals or building and working with the railways. Many had migrated from areas of high levels of unemployment with William's [6] father for example taking up a 20–acre farm in Ullesthorpe, having moved down with all his young family from Fife in Scotland. For others it was working within dual occupations that ensured the next meal arriving on the family table. Jane's father Samuel was working away from home as a watchman for the Midland Railway in 1891. The long–term absence of one of the key figures of the homestead must have resulted in more stressful workloads for mothers, particularly if one of the family members was quite behaviourally disruptive. The abodes of grandparents often became much needed substitute residences alleviating levels of tension.

Life expectancy was far lower than it is today and the heads of some families were widowers or widows who still required occupations in order to run the family budgets. In 1871 George's widowed mother Ann was 'Taking in washing'. Illegitimate births truly left many women in dire straits. Some single mothers remained in their families whereas others found themselves residing in the local workhouse to whom they were chargeable (usually designated by where they themselves had been born). It is within this network of both prosperous and poverty stricken occupational activity, driven by innovative industrial changes that the three Leicestershire asylums were sited.

The Lunatic Asylums Act 1845 made it mandatory for each borough and county to provide adequate asylum accommodation at public expense for its pauper lunatic populations. All the three Leicestershire asylums were rurally sited in the fresh air and away from immediate industrial pollution.

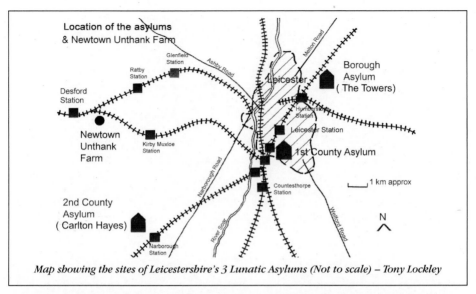

Map showing the sites of Leicestershire's 3 Lunatic Asylums (Not to scale) – Tony Lockley

The 1st Leicestershire County Asylum opened in May 1837, taking over from the smaller Leicester Infirmary Asylum, which had opened 16th April 1794. The establishment was later to be named the Leicestershire and Rutland Asylum. It was sited at the current University of Leicester, with The Fielding Johnson Building and the Superintendent's House still standing. The medical casebook records and reception order certificates of patients aged from 3 to 99 are generally still mainly accessible from January 1845.

Etching of the Leicestershire & Rutland Lunatic Asylum January 1890
University of Leicester Archives ULA/IMA2/2 by James Murray
(the only patient whose full name is given throughout this publication)

1st County Asylum Fielding Johnson Building – Photograph Courtesy of University of Leicester Archives. ULA/FG1/3/10

1st County Asylum Aerial Photograph in 1930's following closure – Photograph courtesy of University of Leicester Archives ULA/FG1/3/96

The Borough Asylum opened in Humberstone in September 1869. It was in later years to be given the name of 'The Towers'. The records for this asylum have not been kept or survived as well as the 1st County Asylum. Most of the full case book records can only be viewed from 1897. Some of these are too damaged to ever refer to. A few earlier patients can be traced via the complete Admission Registers and whose continuing records have spilled over into the later casebooks. Some will of course be much older by this time. It is the age at the time of the initial admission, which places the under fourteen year olds within this research.

Drawing of Borough Asylum - Tony Lockley

The new 2nd County Asylum opened at Narborough in 1907 replacing the 1st Asylum. This mental hospital was given the name of Carlton Hayes circa 1939. The hundred year data protection policies have resulted in only a handful of the young ones being included in this research up until 1912. The study therefore covers in the main, the first two asylums.

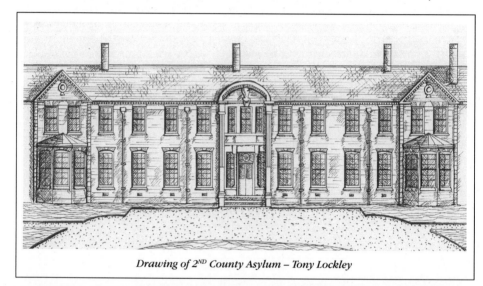

Drawing of 2ND County Asylum – Tony Lockley

2nd County Asylum Recreation HAll on opening day – Photograph Courtesy of Leicestershire, Leicester & Rutland Record Office

Throughout this publication when one of the three Leicestershire asylums is mentioned, they are not always specifically identified as 'which is which' as it is not necessarily immediately relevant to the young ones asylum experiences of the past years.

This historical account is an attempt to tell the true story of one hundred and thirty seven children once, under fourteen years old who were admitted as patients for treatment to one of the three aforementioned asylums in Leicestershire. Their selection for this study was dependant on all or part of their actual medical records still being extant within the Record Office of Leicestershire, Leicester and Rutland.

At the time of admission:–

1 was aged 3
4 were aged 4
9 were aged 5
8 were aged 6
9 were aged 7
8 were aged 8
13 were aged 9
12 were aged 10
15 were aged 11
17 were aged 12
12 were aged 13
29 were aged 14

112 were admitted with the mental disability as then categorised as 'idiots' or 'imbeciles'. The standard terminologies for mental retardation in those years of either an 'idiot' or an 'imbecile', have still been used throughout this research.

An 'idiot' - is an obsolete term for a person of extremely low intelligence, whose intellectual faculties have never been developed, having a mental age of less than 3 years old.

An 'imbecile ' - is an obsolete term for a person of the second order of mental retardation, above the level of idiocy, having a mental age of 7 or 8 years.

The term 'imbecile' appears to be used with far less certainty and there is sometimes a degree of doubt within a diagnosis, especially if epilepsy or a serious accident is also mentioned as a contributor to the condition. There was often considerable discrepancy between the two terms in the case book records and in real life, 'the village idiot' was more commonly 'the village imbecile'. Millicent an 'imbecile' from Knighton, was horrendously teased in her village, prior to her admission. Within this particular group of under fourteens, the term 'congenital' and 'from birth' are constantly used. The phrase 'feeble minded' or the word 'dumb' often compounded the diagnostic difficulties.

The 25 other juveniles were admitted with some form of mental illness – dementia, manias or melancholia often complicated by epilepsy and various other factors. The records of the under fourteen year old admissions that were suffering from these conditions of mental illness were very similar to the entries of adults with similar diagnoses, and they slotted in quite easily alongside the pages of the older patients.

The only difference was that they were so tragically young, to have been afflicted with such high levels of mental illness.

No records of individual programmes have been found. Most of this research has come from finding a line within many other continuous entries on case book pages, such as:–

'Continues in good health'.

'No change in condition'.

Within all these records from a hundred years ago, there are many words and phrases, or terminologies, which are nowadays rarely if ever used. Any significant event related to the asylums was dutifully recorded within other paper work. They were not three asylums with secrets untold. If anything unusual or non–standard happened regarding the patients, the staff, the provisions, the asylum farm, the buildings, gardens or grounds, then a note of it was made in the various superintendents' medical journals or diaries.

The Asylum records from over one hundred years ago provide an incredible insight into the young lives, which were treated within the walls. The entries within the old leather bound journals; often in somewhat archaic text, offer explicit details of the struggles or successes within a patient's short or long–term treatments. The records also continually emphasize, that from its very beginnings, the 1st Leicestershire Asylum, (the most well documented of the three hospitals in this research), was a very progressive institution and was always intended to be a 'House of Cure'.[1] This positive attitude appeared to be there for all; even for the patients who were incurable or the non–starters.

The first under fourteen year old, for whom there are any records of both admission and treatment at an asylum in Leicestershire was Elizabeth Mary, admitted aged 11, from Sparkenhoe in Leicester on 8th March 1845. A severe a bang to the head due to a fall, had resulted in her becoming an epileptic 'imbecile'.

Cheerful Frederick [2], the cover boy is just one of the other 137, who were under fourteen years old at the time of their admission, to one of the three previous Leicestershire Asylums. These 137 have surviving full or part medical case book records giving a description of illness and treatment, or reception order certificates, which are still extant at the Record Office for Leicestershire, Leicester and Rutland.

Frederick [2]

1   Committee of Visitors Prefatory Remarks Rules 1849 Leicestershire's Lunatics H Orme and W Brock Leics Museums and Art Galleries Record Service 1987 ISBN 085022 2273.b

There are 58 other young patients, who were definitely admitted to the 2nd Borough Asylum, whose names are only found within the admission records as their paperwork has either not been kept or is beyond repair. Because the treatment records of such a significant number of admissions are missing, those included in this research are referred to mainly as individuals and not as members of a generalised, statistical group.

To respect the privacy of these young individuals and to avoid any ancestral negativities or embarrassments, only their Christian names are used. They are included throughout the text with just the single, double or treble Christian name or names, which they were given as newborn babies. As there were several with the same name they have also been given an individual identifying number, in brackets after their name, to clarify which is which. Cecil is not though the same admission as Cecil William, as a second name, helps to distinguish between them both. Not only were the names virtually identical like Mabel & Mabel Kezziah, who were admitted three months apart. At times the cropped hairstyles and the uniformity of the clothing led to them having a rather institutionalised appearance. Just over forty young patients have a photographic record still surviving within their case book record following the purchase of photographic equipment, but not all of the later patients have a photograph within their records.

Any reader, who requires any further information, on any of the young patients, can by using the list at the end of the book follow up individual record office reference numbers at the Record Office for Leicestershire, Leicester and Rutland. The number will enable any interested parties to access the documents for themselves. The Access code DE3533 is for admissions to the two County Asylums: The Access code DE2853 is for patients admitted to the Borough Asylum.

The circumstances, which led to the admission of so many tragically young individuals, to what were basically treatment centres for adults were usually unmanageable, unsafe behaviours, or deeply worrying medical conditions. About half of the young ones admitted exhibited severe levels of dangerousness. Many were a danger to themselves; even more were noted as being a danger to others and a significant number were a threat to both themselves and others. Disruptive relatives became increasingly intolerable within the home environment.

The following transcriptions, in chronological order, taken from the individual case book records or reception order certificates from the three asylums, open the doors to the difficulties that families were having to face:

'Constant and uncontrollable propensity to wander without any fixed object in view'. Mary Jane with epileptic mania aged 13 (July 1846)

'He has climbed the wall of the Bridewell in a most daring and wonderful manner and would have frequently repeated the feat, had he not been prevented'. William [7] with epileptic mania aged 14 (November 1850)

'He obeys the call of nature just like an animal, at any time or place', An 'idiot' aged 5 (July 1877)

'Is constantly running away from home and riding by rail without a ticket and can give no explanation of it'. George- [6] an 'imbecile' aged 14 (March 1879)

'Was brought from home by an order by two magistrates in consequence of his father having kept him tied up with a rope'. William [3] *an epileptic 'idiot' aged 14 (December 1879)*

'He has within the last 2 years become unmanageable: he lights matches under the children's beds – takes what is not his and all endeavours of correction apparently have no effect. Early in the year he was sentenced to 14 days for stealing, but was released before his time as not being of sound mind'. Fred an 'imbecile' aged 12 (September 1890)

'Elizabeth his mother says that he is never quiet except at rare intervals when he is asleep. That he has gone four consecutive nights and days this week without sleep and during the past two nights he has only slept about four hours and not at all during the days. He keeps rambling incessantly often saying that Jack the Ripper is in the room'. Frederick [1] *with simple mania aged 13. (February 1891)*

'His mother says he is beyond her control and is not safe to be left for one minute. Has set himself on fire, has attacked and struck the baby and thrown a knife at one of the children. Says she cannot be responsible for him'. Cecil an 'idiot' (March 1897)

'His mother of Railway Houses, Burton Road Oakthorpe, says she dare not leave him on account of his passion, he throws everything into the fire he can get hold of, he will pull his little brother's hair out by hands full and gnaws at his clothes'. Joseph an 'idiot' aged 3. (January 1899).

'Got lost in Leicester for 2 days a week ago – fell off an electric tram and cut his head'. Alfred [1] *an 'imbecile' aged 13. (June 1900)*

'Disturbs the whole neighbourhood – so it is very tiring to be near her on such occasions'. Naomi Millicent an 'idiot' aged 11 (November 1902)

Frances Ann Elizabeth

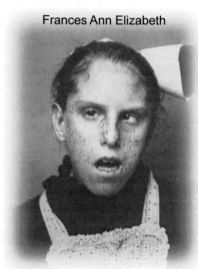

'Of late she is always hanging about the public house door and talking to the boys – usually bad language – cannot dress herself or do anything for herself'. Frances Ann Elizabeth an 'imbecile' aged 14. (August 1902)

'He will pick up anything from the floor and eat it. He will eat grass or flowers and is always in mischief pulling everything to pieces'. Duncan aged 6 (October 1903)

'Took things out of the house and buried them in the fields (packets of nails, cotton etc)'. George [4] *aged 12. (August 1903)*

'There are abundant signs in the house of his destructiveness. The chairs are ripped open, the windows broken'. John Samuel Clifford aged 6 (May 1904).

'He talked in an irrational way, fancied that the worms in the garden followed him about and also that he had taken Carbolic Acid. Points to imaginary objects on the floor'. Walter with mania aged 14 (August 1907).

'Is given to handle her genital organs. She cannot find her way into the house if on the road. Does not realise the necessity of getting out of the way of vehicles. She eats anything including her faeces'. An 'idiot' aged 10 (September 1908).

'He threw the carving knife at her and he has become more mischievous daily. Has to fasten him to the fireguard whilst laying the cloth for meals'. Alfred [2] *aged 10 (May 1908).*

'Noticed yesterday that he had taken a large dose of poison (Atropine and Cocaine)'. William Christmas with melancholia aged 14. (September 1908)

'Says he is always worrying about having knocked a woman on the head with some boards he was carrying, that it got on his nerves, that he has tried to cut his throat'. Charles [3] *with primary dementia aged 14. (December 1910)*

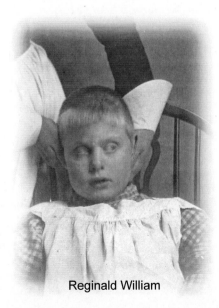

'No intelligent can be obtained, but patient makes hideous noises, bites his hands and slaps his head and face, laughs and tries to smack others'. Reginald William aged 5 (May 1910)

Reginald William

One of the most debilitating members of a Leicestershire family must have been five-year–old Edith in 1890. She would throw things into the fire and knock the other two children about, who were both under three years old. Her reception order certificate, includes behavioural negativities, which were shown to be truly disrupting the pattern of her family life: –

> *'Is restless at night keeping her mother awake and injuring her health and interferes with her getting on with her household duties'.*

For many youngsters, (virtually 10% of them), their previous residence before admission was not their own home, but the local workhouse. A few were noted to be with other family members as workhouse inmates. Some juveniles were recorded as having been in a workhouse for the greater part of their lives, as was the case for Elizabeth [4] aged 10 and Arthur [2] aged 9. Several others were admitted from various Workhouses within Leicestershire. The following excerpts from the casebooks outline some of the sizeable difficulties which resulted in the relocation of certain young work house inmates to an asylum:–

> *'He strikes the infirm inmates with anything he may happen to have in his hands. Is in the habit of pulling the chairs from under the inmates when at meals with the intention of hurting them. Has lately become unmanageable there, throws things about, plays with fire'. Bertie aged 13. (August 1902 Uppingham Union)*

> *'She is stated to have been destructive in the Union House breaking plates and glass'. Millicent aged 11. (August 1860 Narborough Union)*

> *'Has been an idiot from birth and spent most of her life in Lutterworth Union, has been boarded out lately but became so troublesome, that she was sent back to the Union, has lately been unmanageable and bites and kicks and scratches other patients in the ward. Is an illegitimate child her mother and brother are both imbeciles'. Elizabeth [4] aged 10. (October 1891 Lutterworth Union)*

The Union Matron and a male porter both reported to the doctor on admission, that Bertie was constantly playing tricks on the older men. Some like young Emily [1] had never known any other home than Market Bosworth Union House. She was admitted as a <u>foundling</u> (the term was actually underlined in the records). One has to wonder the reasons for her relocation to an asylum as she was recorded as:–

> *'Amiable and gentle - clean in habits, affectionate and mute but not deaf'.*

There were various reasons why infants and young teenagers were admitted into lunatic asylums in Leicestershire many years ago. It cannot be overlooked that there were not the same family support networks as there are today and it was usually because family members or other carers, were no longer coping with the often formidable task of looking after them. There were often large families to bring up too. To take just one example Mary Ann an 'idiot' was admitted the same day as her mother Emma. There were sixteen children in their family. The parents, who had to view and cope with the continual horrendous, convulsive, epileptic episodes of their young ones, must have been living in a nightmare. Dealing with incontinence before more modernised laundry facilities and synthetic fabrics must have been a daunting task, for an already busy mother.

Many hard working parents were often also up against intensifying household poverty. Children were expected to contribute to family life at quite a young age. Even if they were just performing ancillary tasks such as stoking stoves, fetching wood, collecting water or taking their father's dinners, they were still effectively enabling a higher standard of living for the family unit. The very youngest who were able to be given child–sized occupations, could still in a small way be economic contributors within their household. As they grew older there were even more expectations for their potential earning power either in the household production unit or in occupations outside the family walls.

These were the days of open fires and open doors, which sadly did not go hand in hand with youngsters who had minimum concepts of safety. In the days before central heating, the danger of the very necessary open fire for heating and cooking is constantly mentioned in the admission paper work. There are two consecutive admissions in the 1st County Asylum records in 1862, Elizabeth [2] aged 8 and William [4] aged 7– One would get into the family fire, the other would set himself on fire by putting his clothes in the fire. The open doors of many decades ago also caused formidable difficulties.

The relief that the asylums afforded to families who were unable to cope can never be overlooked. After a local Workhouse, there was essentially nowhere else for the young of many years ago with severe mental illness or learning difficulties to be, if they were essentially going to be free and not secured for their own safety.

Children are not always expected to be perfectly behaved within everyday family experiences, but some of the continual, extreme and totally insubordinate actions of the young mentally impaired of yester year, must have been way beyond the behavioural modification capacities of the average devoted parent. As they grew older disruptive family members became more intolerable within a family unit and perhaps more embarrassing individuals within an urban or rural community. Even though seriously dysfunctional behaviours could be modified and certain clinical symptoms could be successfully treated, a high percentage of these youngsters from many years ago were technically not curable.

'Was it the push of the family or the pull of the asylum'.[2]

---

2   The History of Psychiatry Edward Shorter John Wiley and Sons 978–0–471–24531–5

Initial Assessments Prior To An Asylum Admission

When insurmountable problems arose in families or the local workhouse, help was fortunately at hand. It was usually the local doctor who was the immediate instigator of any help. This local medical man often had the dual occupation, of holding the post of the community's Relieving Officer too. The Relieving Officer's task was to compile and complete the reception order certificate. As a leading figure, he was also there for families who were extremely worried about their off spring's mental illness. It is not known how he became aware of the need for assistance. He may have known certain youngsters from much earlier stages in their childhood. These were the days before the National Health Service, with families if they could afford it, probably joining some form of local sick club. Someone needed to help the young ones who were becoming an overwhelming and usually disruptive problem in their urban or rural communities.

Patients could not just arrive at the asylum for treatment, in order to free parents or workhouse officials, from impossible maladjusted behavioural situations. No admission to an asylum could be completed or be legal, without a written medical assessment and a doctor's signature. The Reception Orders were probably viewed by many as a virtual rescue from what was essentially 24 hours a day surveillance of their off springs or inmates – every hour of the day, every single day of the week, every month of the year. The parents' failure to cope with certain family members, obviously played a strategic role in the decision making. The Relieving Officer (frequently shortened to 'RO'), was the key figure in both acknowledging the depth of the individual difficulties and arranging assistance. The young asylum newcomers themselves were complete outsiders to the final judgment or the decision making for an admission. Parents being seriously ill or a parent having just died influenced certain admissions.

In order to make an accurate assessment, the usual procedure was for the 'RO' to call round to make observations on individual behaviours in household, workhouse situations or even at times police and prison cells. He was then able to judge whether admission to an asylum was appropriate. . One of the clearest assessments comes with the admission of the very youngest, the three year old infant Joseph, from Railway Cottages in Oakthorpe:-

*'In reply to your enquiry I must say I can not add any other fact more clearly indicating insanity observed by myself at the time of the examination, though my visit was of an hours duration. The child being dumb and of **such tender years** made matters somewhat difficult, but after getting history of the case from the parents. I had no hesitation of filling in the certificate'. Edmund John Thompson Relieving Officer* [3]

---

3   Part of a letter within the Reception Order Certificate for Joseph. Courtesy of Record Office for Leicestershire, Leicester and Rutland DE3533–237

Another assessment is given in the following excerpt, which is taken from the Reception Order Certificate of seven year old William [4] from Shepshed (then spelt Sheepshed).

'I the undersigned, being a member of the Royal College of Surgeons and a Licentiate Of the Society of Apothecaries, both of London and being in actual practise as a Surgeon and Apothecary hereby certify that I on the fifth day of February at Sheepshed in the County of Leicester, personally examined William of Sheepshed and that the said William is a Lunatic and a proper Person to be taken charge of and detained under Care and Treatment, and that I have formed this opinion upon the following grounds: viz. -

Facts indicating Insanity observed by myself *– He is in continual restlessness, not appearing to have any control over his actions.*

Other Facts indicating Insanity communicated to me by others *– Have been told by his mother that he is exceedingly violent. That on several occasions he has set himself on fire, by putting his clothes in the fire.*

Signed James Wood'[4]

Another inclusion in the casebooks records, is taken from a Regional Officer's report and comes at the time of the admission of Arthur [6] who was admitted with epileptic mania In October 1909:–

'He was playing in Roberts Road and came to meet me, but a few minutes afterwards could not tell whether I had been walking or driving or whether we entered by front or back door. He said this was his birthday, which I am informed is not the case. He suddenly began to take off his coat and stopped as suddenly. On a previous date I saw him recovering from an epileptic fit'.

When the 'RO' went to visit 10 year old Elsie in Ashby Workhouse, he had quite a compassionate response:–

'The last time I tried to have a chat with her she had her head down and seemed frightened, so I could get nothing out of her'.

The 'RO' not only made observations, he also performed various medical examinations. Edgar William was not the easiest of children to assess:–

'Whilst being examined he tried to put his feet through the fire guard.'

One of the sadder inclusions from an 'RO' was for William [9]:–

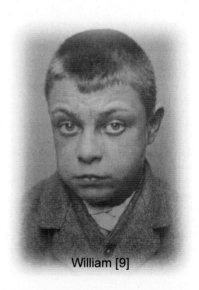

William [9]

'Found him tied down to a chair, otherwise he would rush out and get on the line at the Railway Station'. Relieving Officer Certificate -

For one of the assessments a Dr Alfred Payne had gone round to William Christmas's (2nd Christian name as he was born on Christmas day) master's house also a doctor in London Road, Leicester. Accuracy was always the intention and for William Christmas who was diagnosed as to be suffering from melancholia, the investigations became a virtual inquisition:–

'Change of manner lately: statement that he felt strange in his head lately and had a fear of doing himself harm.

By Marie Young employer's child 148 London Road:– He had talked to her about suicide and had threatened her with a heavy parcel and a carving knife, slightly injuring her with it.

By Sarah Bradshaw Servant 29 Melbourne Street - Statement that 'Me and Sarah are going to play hanging' That he had put a towel round her neck from behind.

By Mrs Lois Newick mother 48 York Road - That he has often been strange, depressed refusing to speak. That he has made rambling remarks today'. Admitted 21st September[5] 1908

One of the important legal questions to be completed on the reception order was – 'By whose authority sent'. The most significant people in authority were the Regional Officers but there were almost always two other significant people. The other influential individual was usually a Justice of the Peace, or a local vicar or mayor who was a 'JP' too. There were a few admission certificates that had the signatures of others:–

Albert Isaac - Justice of the Peace and the Visitors of the Leicestershire and Rutland County Asylum

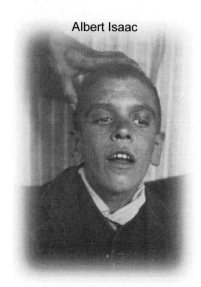

Albert Isaac

William [3] - Required the Justice of the Peace and two Magistrates as he too had been found tied up with rope.

Three young patients, Ann and Jonathan (both with epileptic mania), and Mary [2] (with 'idiocy') were actually admitted under the authority of their own fathers together with the Regional Officer's signature. If they were transferred from another care environment, there were usually signatures from both locations. When Betsy was transferred from Wakefield there were four signatures in all, to

---

5   1st County Asylum Reception Order Certificates. DE3533–241

24

successfully complete her documentation.

A very few young ones were admitted as private patients but the majority were admitted as paupers. Maria [1] had been afflicted with 'idiocy', from birth, and had initially in July 1847 been admitted as a private patient at the age of 7:–

> *'When the friends have however become unequal to the payment of expenses in consequence of which she was removed, thrown upon her parish, readmitted, the same day as a Pauper chargeable to the Leicester Union.'*

An inclusion within the 1st County Asylum Charity Ledger gives details of the cost incurred usually by a Parish for treatment in an asylum.[6] The following figures are for Maria Martha:–

June 25th 1881 7 weeks at 10/– £3.10.0	£3.15.3 Paid by cash 21st July 1881
Sept 24th 1881 13 weeks at 10/– £6.10	£7.4.11d Paid by cash October 22nd 1881
Dec 24th 1881 13 weeks at 10/– £6.10	£6.13.3d Paid by cash Jan 19th 1882
Mar 25th 1882 6 weeks at 10/– £3.00	£3.2.6 Paid by cash June 24th 1882

It is impossible to say how the admission to an asylum, was experienced for any of the patients, let alone those who were so young. For many, their only previous experiences of daily life will have been living in the same rural or urban household, with maybe some other regular contact with the close relatives, the family friends, neighbours and their households. Those who had spent a fraction of their young lives in a Union House may have been less traumatised by relocation to an asylum. The wards, run by unknown faces, will though have been totally strange to the majority of young newcomers at the time of their admission.

---

6   1st County Asylum Charity Ledger QS107/2/5

The Admission Process

The admission process got under way once all the legal paperwork was in place. Any irregularities with the certificate often called for the patient's admission being refused and them having to be readmitted later, (sometimes the same day) when the paper work was correct. The asylum clinician himself could only assess the appropriateness of any admission from paperwork completed by a doctor from outside the walls. The Reception Order completed by the Regional Officer, was one exceptionally vital piece of paper as at time of entry, it was often the only information that the Asylum Medical Admission Officer was going to get on some incoming patients. This was particularly true if significant family members were not accompanying their son or daughter, at the time of admission. With outside paper work completed and a successful application for an available place made, the young ones would arrive. If the asylums were full, there must have been some form of waiting list.

The young admissions arrived, as all new patients did, usually on Wednesdays or Saturdays, generally between 11.00 am and 2.00 pm. They were taken through the gates, perhaps helped off a carriage and into a room, with at least one accompanying adult, who would have been carrying the Reception Order Certificate, which was the vital entry ticket for admission. It was the piece of paperwork that required the mentally disadvantaged young ones to be classified as 'insane', 'a person of unsound mind' or a 'lunatic': The incoming patient immediately activated an information gathering session, which was all to be dutifully recorded. A man with extensive medical qualifications would have been seated at a desk, ready to initiate the paper work. His face was probably going to be the first of what would be a succession of strange faces. (Thomas [7] obviously believed the assessing medical officer was going to be his new employer, for he declared, at the time of his admission, that 'he was not going to work for him').

On the desk in front of the Medical Officer would have been a large leather bound case book ledger opened at the next, completely data free, totally blank page. The subsequent script was to become the very first entry on the incoming individual's own page, a fresh admission number, for personal identification purposes. (The format and lay out of the case book pages are shown of the first young patient's still extant records on the following pages) The books were very big as can be seen from the image below. (Each one is approximately 400 millimetres by 300 millimetres and about 50 millimetres thick). Initially both males and females were recorded in the same book but subsequently males and females were recorded in separate books. The size of the pages may perhaps have encouraged the vast extent of the subsequent record keeping.

Throughout the decades of the running of both asylums the arrangement, the wording and the lay out of the informative enquiries did change. The 1st County Asylum case books (26 of them in all) have survived far better (from 2nd January 1845) than the fellow Borough Asylum Records. Each of the 26 County Asylum Case Books contained information on between 150 to 300 admissions.

No.	The Christian and Surname, at length, of the Patient.	Age.	Place of Abode.	Class or Parish.	Occupation or Profession.
593	Elizabeth Mary	11	Belgrave Leicester	4th Class	none

When did this attack commence?	From Infancy
Was it preceded by any severe or long-continued mental emotion or exertion?	No -
Did it succeed any serious illness or accident affecting the nervous system?	It succeeded a severe fall -
Is it consequent on pregnancy, parturition, or lactation?	No -
Has it arisen or been accompanied by any irregularity of the uterine functions?	No
Has the Patient suffered from former attacks of the disease? and, if so, how long were the intervals of sanity?	Has been afflicted from Infancy -
What is the supposed cause of the malady?	An Injury to the head -
Has the Patient attempted self-destruction or violence towards others?	Has been very violent to others
Is the Patient prone to tear clothes, or break furniture?	Yes
Has the Patient refused to take food?	No but will eat any thing destructive -
Are the Habits of the Patient cleanly?	No -
Is the Patient subject to Fits or Palsy?	Yes. Epileptic Fits -
Does the Patient labour under any other Disease?	No -
What is the state of the general health?	Good -
Has any Relative of the Patient been insane?	An Aunt was confined in this asylum
What are the deranged ideas or mental hallucinations under which the Patient has laboured?	This poor child is nearly reduced to a state of idiocy in consequence of the injury she sustained from a fall and the fits which were consequent upon it. During the paroxysms of violence which characterize the attacks of epileptic mania she requires constant care to prevent injury to herself and others. Ever after the intervals however between the fits she is an active, lively little creature but totally devoid of Intellectuality
By whose authority sent?	Friends and the Order of a Visitor March 8th 1845 -
Medical Certificate.	William Crossley Irwin - Surgeon - March 8 - 1845 -

Earliest surviving case book page for Elizabeth Mary (See overleaf for typed transcription)

No	The Christian name and Surname, at length, of the patient	Age	Place of Abode	Class or Parish	Occupation or Profession
593	*Elizabeth Mary*	*11*	*Sparkenhoe Leicester*	*4th Class*	*None*

When did the attack commence?	*From infancy*
Was it preceded by any long–continued mental exertion or emotion	*No*
Did it succeed any serious illness or accident affecting the nervous system?	*It succeeded a severe fall*
Is it consequent on pregnancy, parturition or lactation	*No*
Has it arisen or been accompanied by any irregularity of the uterine functions	*No*
Has the patient suffered from former attacks of the disease? And if so how long were the intervals of sanity?	*Has been afflicted from infancy*
What is the supposed cause of the malady?	*An injury to the head*
Has the patient attempted self–destruction or violence towards others?	*Has been violent to others*
Is the patient prone to tear clothes or break furniture?	*Yes*
Has the patient refused to take food?	*No –but will eat anything destructive*
Are the habits of the patient cleanly?	*No*
Is the Patient subject to Fits or Palsy?	*Yes – epileptic fits*
Does the Patient labour under any other disease?	*No*
What is the state of the general health?	*Good*
Has any Relative of the Patient been insane?	*An aunt was confined in this asylum*
What are the deranged ideas or mental hallucinations under which the Patient has laboured?	*This poor child is nearly reduced to the state of idiocy in consequence of the injury she sustained from a fall and the fits that were consequent upon it. During the paroxysms of violence, which characterize the attacks of epileptic mania she requires constant care to prevent injury to herself and others – during the intervals however – between the fits – she is an active lively little creature but totally devoid of intellectuality.*
By whose authority sent	*Friends and the Order of a Visitor March 8th 1845*
Medical Certificate	*William Crossley Irwin Surgeon March 8th 1845*

The first personal details gathered, even for the potentially incurable, and the juveniles with learning difficulties, showed the institution always held fast to its early ideals. that the patients should leave totally cured or much relieved. Some of the most strategic words within the paper work for the 1st County Asylum were that, it was always intended to be (Block capitals as used in report):–

'A HOUSE OF CURE and NOT A HOUSE OF DETENTION'.[7]

The young Patients were entering buildings, which were essentially intended for another age group, as were in many ways the investigative enquiries within the paper work, both prior to and actually on admission. Did the 1st County Asylum contemplate the arrival of almost fifty children aged ten and under, when somebody was designing the format of the pages, before the orders of the case books for printing? It is obvious from the innumerable non–informative dashes, 'not knowns' or totally blank spaces, that many of the enquiries were wholly inappropriate, particularly with regard to the young 'idiot' or 'imbecile' admissions and their life histories.

It is very evident from the initial entries, which the resident Medical Officer entered at the time of admission that he had attempted to gather every possible piece of information. He must have gleaned whatever he could from the Reception Order Certificates especially if any accompanying adult was not present. The County and Asylum case book pages were similar but not identical with the certificate's investigative queries. The 'RO' certificates were though sometimes, quite scant and basic in any facts they offered on the incoming Patient:–

'Unmistakable idiocy'. - Henry [3] *- Frank Fullager* MRCS LAC [8]

As can be seen from the replication of a case book sheet (on the preceding pages) there were many sections requiring completion

Previous residence at the time of admission

Over a third came from addresses either in Leicester itself or villages quite close to the town centre. About a quarter of the other infants and juveniles had considerable distances to travel to gain admission. They came from the county market towns of Ashby de la Zouch, Hinckley, Lutterworth, Market Harborough, Melton Mowbray and Oakham or they came from distant villages such as Swinford (near Rugby) or Redmile a village on the Nottinghamshire & Leicestershire border.

About 20 did not arrive from home, but were being relocated from the Union Workhouses of Leicestershire. The majority of the younger patients arriving from a Union House had not been inmates in the company of other family members. Elizabeth's [3] mother and brother though, were all imbeciles and residents together. Both Elsie and Bertie were with their mothers in a workhouse. William [8] had been admitted to a Union because of his mother's death and Sarah Jane became an inmate due to both her parents having fallen seriously ill.

7   Committee of Visitors Prefatory Remarks Rules 1849 Leicestershire's Lunatics H Orme and W Brock Leics Museums and Art Galleries Record Service 1987 ISBN 085022 2273.
8   1st County Asylum Reception Order Certificates DE3533–228

Once the new Borough Asylum opened in 1869, it sent round paper flyers to other asylums, advertising places, in a new more modern location, if they were needed. The most significant young admissions from a more distant location were the 24 that were admitted from addresses in Derby and six of that number were aged just six, with another 5 arriving from Nottingham. What will they have made of that long ride in a horse drawn vehicle? It is impossible to assess whether the trek for treatment, was a traumatic experience or an exciting adventure that was enjoyed. One who had to travel the longest distance from Yorkshire, was young Betsy⁻

> *'I hereby certify that Betsy..... is in a fit state of bodily health to travel from this asylum to Leicester'. John Botterill Esq and Joseph Bowser Relieving Officer -' She is not competent in keeping herself from harm'. Father's address No 12 Waggitts Court Primrose Street Leeds Asylum Stanley cum Wrenthorpe in the County of York. A Pauper Lunatic chargeable to the Parish of Market Harborough.*[9]

Some of the later journeys would have been by steam–powered vehicle. George [5] who had arrived from Melton Mowbray in May 1905, was noted of being easily frightened and that included the train journey he had made for admission to the 1st County Asylum.

A couple of the new young inmates appear to have been brought to the asylum from prison or directly from court, possibly with officials from the police or the county jail. Henry [1] according to a newspaper cutting adhered to his case book page[10], had stabbed his mother quite severely and attacked his sister too.

At Leicester on Saturday, Henry Hancock, 14, son of a farmer, was charged with attempting to murder his mother. The lad greatly annoyed his sister, who complained to his mother. The boy then attempted to secure a gun to shoot his sister, but he was prevented in this, and was punished by his mother. He then seized a knife and deliberately stabbed his mother in the side, inflicting a dangerous wound. She lost a great deal of blood, and her life was at one time in great danger. Evidence was given showing that the lad was of weak intellect, and he was ordered to be removed to a lunatic asylum.

Ten years later in November 1898 there is the following entry in his records:–

> *'Cannot be employed in any way, is a poor feeble idiot boy and one would hardly credit him with the designs and actions recorded in the newspaper cutting on the opposite page'.*[11]

Edmund had been waiting trial at the County Prison for stealing a horse and trap. He had been on remand for over 6 weeks, but was found to be insane so he was sent to the County Asylum, probably not in the company of his parents in February 1884. One also has to wonder who came in with young William[3], who was brought from home, by an order given by two magistrates, in consequence of his father having kept him

9 County Asylum Reception Order Certificates DE3533–228
10 Newspaper Cutting adhered to Henry's [1] case book page. Courtesy of the Record Office for Leicestershire, Leicester and Rutland DE3533–198–4901
11 1st County Asylum Case Books DE3533–198–4901

tied up with rope. (There were two Williams admitted to an asylum due to this form of restraint.)

The residence at the time of admission was usually home with the name and abode of their nearest relative also had to be given. It was usually the father and their home address. John William's [1] father had given 6 consecutive contact addresses in Melton, Kettering, Woolwich, Cardiff, Sleaford and Southampton. Most of those admitted from Union Houses had their home address included too. Orphans like William [8] would obviously not have a home address. George [4] an 'imbecile' whose father had just vanished 3 months before his asylum admission in August 1903, had a guardian's name and address entered.

George [4]

Previous History

For some case book admissions the existence of a 'Previous History' section was there to be completed and it also gave some clues as to whether the infants and juveniles had arrived in the company of a family member. For some, the parents were very definitely present at the time of admission. John Samuel Clifford's photograph of admission may have been taken with his father, as it was usually only an adult's steadying hands that are part of the image.

John Samuel Clifford

When the previous history section is completely blank (as was the case with young Duncan), this may be because no close relatives accompanied the new young entrant. When the phrase 'from mother' is entered it cannot be definitely taken that any following details, were given to the doctor at the asylum on entry, but it was probably the case. For Janet Winnie her grandmother gave the previous history. A young Bertie had been brought up by his grandparents.

The parents of Emma [2] who is admitted suffering from epileptic mania get an incredibly positive 'write up':–

> *The father and mother are remarkable for their quiet and respectable conduct as well as their active and industrious habits'.*

It was not necessarily beneficial of course for such young patients to eventually have to bid a total farewell to their parents at the actual asylum, at the time of their admission.

Charles [2] admitted with dementia, clung desperately to his father and begged him to take him away from the asylum. Any accompanying adult would be intensely questioned, in order to aid any future treatment programmes. There was likely to be less information for the youngsters who were being relocated from a Union Workhouse, particularly those who had been long–term residents in one. It is quite understandable that a Union House staff member would not have had the same depths of information that a parent would have had.

The section of 'Previous History' often included details on any former schooling. A young individual's intellectual powers usually coincided with any education they had received. The normal pattern of a child's life, was after all to spend a considerable proportion of their time, learning within their local educational establishment, if there was one readily available. Edward an 'idiot' had evidently had schooling at a Union House, or had been taken from there to a school:–

'Cruelty to the other boys in the school injuring them and once attempting to strangle a lad with his braces, prevented by the schoolmaster who had lots more of these circumstances'.

Only a handful of incoming young patients have any mention of having ever gone to school. Of those having access to the normal educational opportunities, most of their initial diagnostic conditions were either recorded as epileptic imbeciles or they were suffering from mania, simple mania, melancholia or dementia.

Walter James had been scholastically progressing quite well until he suffered from epilepsy brought on by a severe attack of measles. One Thomas [6] (who had been run over at the age of 5) had only reached the '2nd Standard'. William [6] an 'imbecile', who had been affected by epilepsy four years previously was recorded as 'a fairly sharp boy at school'. Those who went to school and to some degree achieved some level of success within the achievements of the time, referred to, as 'Standards' were generally those who were not afflicted from birth.

For the majority of the admissions, there is absolutely no information on any achievement within learning. There is potentially a less negative achievement within a total blank. Certain positive information could have failed to be included. Violet Anne a young epileptic, 'hydrocephalic' admission was one such case, as she had never been able to go to school. Fred had been to school 'but was not kept strictly to work on account of his fits'. William [9] who was an epileptic 'imbecile', was recorded as having gone 'to a school for this, but they could make nothing of him'. A handful have totally negative inclusions on any former schooling and had never been able to learn anything at an educational establishment.

The written inclusions for young Elizabeth's [3] condition taken from the Relieving Officer's certification records (21st October 1896) are very questionably intriguing. She was on admission recorded as just an epileptic but had apparently formerly been viewed by the 'RO' as a congenital 'idiot'. Her father had previously died from general paralysis:–

'The child was like any other and had passed the 3rd and 4th standard at school. A year ago she became irritable and the doctor was under the impression that

mental work was injuring the child and he advised her to be removed and kept at home for some time. The patient could run around like any other child until October last when weakness of the legs supervened or paralysed condition soon set in'.

A few are recorded with achievements in the three 'Rs' but there is no information on where they learnt these skills. John [4] 'knew his letters but could not read the simplest word'. It would have been expected that the mentally ill had higher cognitive skills than the young with noticeable learning difficulties. Thomas [6] with simple mania was 'certainly a little below the average in intelligence of boy of his age and station'.

Duration of existing attack

The 'duration of attack' enquiry section, virtually becomes a diagnostic confirmation, for the more serious mental handicap of 'idiocy', with the section for almost all of these patients being riddled with the words 'congenital' or phrases such as 'from birth' or 'afflicted since infancy'. . There are a number of inclusions, where the age of the child is equal to how long they have been in that condition. John William [1] aged 5 had been an 'idiot' for 5 years, Duncan aged 6 an 'idiot' for 6 years and many others for the ages of 7,8,9 and 10 years. The most tragic entry, actually written as a full sentence, is for John William [4] – 'Duration of existing attack life'.

In contrast to the admissions of those with learning difficulties, the records for the young mentally ill, are painfully similar to the patterns of the entries for the adult admissions. Their pages for admission are not continually sparse, completely blank or have just a dash. The duration of illness enquiries were of far more relevance to the 25, under fourteen years olds, who were suffering from some form of mental illness at a very young age. The length of time a mental condition has been endured for these young individuals is comparable in many ways again, to the details given for the adult patients. The following details are far more within the trend of the normal case book entries:–

Mary Ann [1]	aged 14 – Simple mania –	For 12 months
Charles [3]	aged 14 – Primary dementia –	For 6 months
Maria [2]	aged 14 – Chronic mania –	For 11 weeks
Charles [2]	aged 14 – Dementia –	For 6 months
William Christmas	aged 14 – Melancholia –	For 3 months
Elizabeth [1]	aged 12 – Acute mania –	For some weeks

Rank, Profession of Previous Occupation if any

There was also a section to record a patient's occupation before their admission. The nearest many of those with learning difficulties got to being accredited with an actual occupation, was to be a 'labourer's son', the 'child of washerwoman' or a 'school boy'. The young mentally ill had understandably been far more employable.

The previous occupations of the young patients are quite diverse. George [1] admitted at the age of 14, suffering from chronic mania had been a billiard maker before his admission to an asylum. Frederick [1] had been working for two years as a biscuit maker

within a biscuit factory. Three weeks before his admission his parents had noted that
he had started to look out of sorts with him also being in a very dull frame of mind. He
had continued his employment up until a week prior to admission, when he had started
to continually chatter a lot of nonsense. Charles's [2] life followed the normal pattern of
any 13 year old. . He had left school to become employed at a shoe factory punching toe
caps:–

> *'About 6 months ago became changed mentally, was forgetful and confused –
> would leave his work in the morning after half an hour and go home and when
> spoken to – said he did not know he was at home and would run back to work
> again. Had to give up work some weeks ago. Since then has been at home – often
> would not go out'.*

Walter was a tailor, Charles [3] was an errand boy, Mary [3] a domestic servant and Maria
[2] was a seamer (perhaps in her own home environment). Thomas [7] from Navigation
Street, Leicester admitted suffering from mania had been a labourer for the Borough. He
was constantly wishing to go off and sign up to be a soldier and consequently appeared
to take absolutely no interest in anything else. Another teenager named Thomas [6],
admitted from Loughborough Union House, had no occupation noted, but he would
have undoubtedly, if well enough have been expected to work with other inmates in the
Union's basic mundane industrial tasks. Harriett's diminutive appearance, had though
sadly led to her being exhibited about the country, as a 'Talking Monkey'.

Religious persuasion

From June 1856 there was an opportunity or a requirement, to include the patients
individual religious faiths. For just over a hundred, there was a box available to record
their religion, on their case book sheets. Almost seventy percent of the young with
learning difficulties have absolutely no religion recorded and it is immediately evident
from the actual entries just how few 'idiots' or 'imbeciles' were recorded as having
an opportunity to practise a religious faith. Even though there is a possibility that the
asylum doctors believed that a certain degree of intellect was required to practise
Christianity, and there was therefore, no point in making any enquiries as to which
faith was followed. The figures for 'idiots' with a religion are particularly low. Would
the 'village idiot' be taken to Sunday services? Were assumptions made that they would
not have been taken to church or chapel for fears of embarrassment or of behaviours
disrupting worship? Parents were generally very proud of their particular family faiths
and some may have thought it quite natural to include everyone in their household.
There must have been considerable satisfaction in the knowledge, that the asylum
officer's quill was connecting a specific religion such as 'Wesleyan Reformist' with
their family. Proportionately, the figures for youngsters recorded with a particular faith
were similar to the numbers of adults within certain doctrines – most were Church of
England, fewer were non–conformist dissenters and just a few were Roman Catholic.

Whether subject to epilepsy

One of the most strategic enquires in the case book records, was centred on any
evidence of epilepsy. It was the clinical condition, which most commonly, further
complicated the mental state of any patient at the time of admission. For a few of the
youngsters epilepsy was actually given as the reason for the mental defect or illness,

with Edgar William's 'idiocy' being directly accredited to infantile convulsions. For some the epilepsy had been so severe that they had required, prior to asylum admission, treatment in other hospitals, with Thomas [1] aged 6 from Ellistown, having been admitted to the 1st County Asylum from the Leicester Royal Infirmary in August 1907, as he was experiencing 12 fits a day.

There was tremendous variation of the epileptic experience within each individual's record, with a slightly higher percentage of boys being affected than girls. For some it was tragically the eventual main reason for a young individual's admission. Over twenty young patients were admitted with mania of some form, with a high proportion of that number being specifically recorded with 'epileptic mania'. The average age of this group of youngsters on entry was thirteen and a half. For others almost a hundred of them, it was a case of 'epilepsy too', as an added extra. Their other condition was some degree of developmental impairment. Several others were more specifically recorded– 34 with some form of 'idiocy' plus epilepsy (average age on admission just below 9 years) and 40 with some form of 'imbecility' plus epilepsy (with their average age on admission being almost 12).

The young patients had been 'afflicted' with epilepsy for various lengths of time. Some were recorded as having a 'predisposition from birth' with 5 'idiots' or 'imbeciles' specifically recorded as suffering from epilepsy directly from birth. The infant Frederick [2] had had fits since he was 3 days old and Mabel from 4 months, Thomas [4] from 2 years of age. Four of the girls, only had records of fits whilst they were teething in their early years. For many it appears to be the actual condition of mental handicap, which is recorded as being 'congenital' or 'from birth', with no clear details of when the epileptic symptoms themselves commenced. Just over 20 admissions are specific to how long epileptic fits have been evident within the child's lifetime.

The epileptic condition had such a noted reputation, that at times epilepsy seems to have been used as a way of gaining a place within the asylum. It was another form of 'black mark' at the time of admission, which appears to have swayed the ultimate decision, to be given a place. Frederick's [1] mother told the doctor on his admission that he had two fits on the previous afternoon, about an hour apart. Absolutely no epilepsy is recorded within his following case book entries. Uppingham Union Workhouse staff, obviously wanted the troublesome Bertie to be relocated, as he was positively noted as being subject to epilepsy, but there is yet again no evidence of fits shown within his records. There are several new admissions where on the first record of entry, the epilepsy box either has the word 'yes' or 'a tick' included but later records are a continuation of 'no fits yet' (Stanley William was one such case). Unfortunately, a few soon showed a propensity for the affliction. The epilepsy records for Albert were exactly the opposite – It was a case of epilepsy 'No' and not previously diagnosed at the time of admission in 1902. The first time fits were mentioned for him was five years later and the 2nd mention of epilepsy is within his eventual Cause of Death – 'Status epilepticus' in October 1910.

For others quite specific, single events had been noted as a cause for the onset of their convulsions. Frederick [1] admitted with simple mania was recorded:–

> *When he was ten years old he is said to have had sunstroke: he was out most of the day bathing when it was very hot and was a good deal exposed: when*

he came home his mother said he was very queer and partially insensible and had been under two doctors for it. Since then he has never been quite the same lad and it was found difficult to get him a position in which to get his own livelihood'.

For several others it was some form of accident that was the cause of subsequent 'fits'. Muriel Gertrude from Measham had fallen from her high chair on to her head when 3 months old. John Samuel Clifford an 'idiot' had also had a bad fall when 3 months. Several youngsters were recorded with potentially hereditary influences to their epileptic condition.

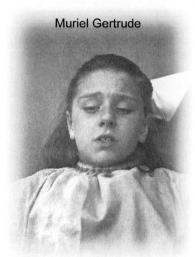

Muriel Gertrude

The incoming young admissions sometimes had their epilepsy attributed to specific times in their growth and development. For some of the female teenagers it was noted that fits were more likely at the time of the monthly periods. For Elizabeth Mary, quite clear records were made relating to her epilepsy and her menstruation: –

'It was hoped at the age of puberty that the menstrual secretion would have materially relieved the head affection, so far from this being the case, it was clear that if the fits of epilepsy were diminished in frequency they certainly were increased in intensity, and upon the occurrence of the burning heat which characterised this months for nearly a week she had fifteen to twenty fits in a day and not withstanding every remedy used, nothing stayed their progress or mitigated their violence and at length she sunk completely exhausted from them'.

Toileting Skills and Cleanliness

After details on epilepsy, one of the most common inclusions on the first page of entry, for any of the young ones with 'idiocy' or 'imbecility', was details on their individual toileting skills, which were usually referred to as their 'habits'. The most common occurring phrase was 'Is wet and dirty in habits', and it is probably because they could not control either their urine or faeces. Just as many of the young 'idiots' are noted to be just 'dirty', but this may have been referring to both bodily functions. Other words were used to define the lack of achievement in this situation – 'degraded', 'neglectful', 'uncleanly', 'defective', or 'spare' – Two were noted to be inattentive to the calls of, or unable to attend to the ordinary wants of nature. One lad was dirty in his habits, passing urine and faeces anywhere and even eating the latter if he was not prevented. A multiply–handicapped male had the most negative inclusion for toileting awareness:–

'Passes faeces and urine apparently without consciousness'.

It was usually those classified as 'idiots' who had little or no control over these bodily functions. A female 'imbecile' was perhaps not completely trained as she was recorded as – 'Her habits are almost idiotic.' A few were all written to be neglectful if they were not carefully watched and tended to.

The 'imbeciles' appear generally to have been expected to be clean and William [6], Henry [2], Betsy, George [6], Elizabeth [4] were just a few so recorded. Some 'imbeciles' may have been so expected to be clean, that no mention was made of their toileting achievements in the asylum records and in this area of their development they were considered to be essentially normal. A few 'idiots' such as Sarah Susan Ravina, Ethela Isola and Ida Winifred were also noted positively in this area of their development.

Parental efforts with any toilet training were at times quite negatively recorded within the records, as was the case with a 7 year old admitted in April 1868:–

> *'She has evidently been improperly brought up, not having been corrected in her dirty habits, such as wetting herself when standing up and apparently thinking she is doing nothing improper'.*

Those admitted at an older age, may though have been able to benefit from longer parental toilet training programmes in their own homes.

Whether Suicidal

One of the most tragic questions for any patient at the time of admission was as to whether they had any evidence of suicidal tendencies. A few of the young ones did tragically show a propensity towards them taking their own life, earning them on admission, a tick in the 'If Suicidal' box. Persons so classified were sited in a special ward usually together with the severe epileptics, so that they would be on a more careful twenty–four hour watch by the staff.

Many who had exhibited exceptionally dangerous patterns of behaviour in their former environment were recorded to be suicidal. John [2] if left alone frequently attempted to get into the family fire. Another lad named John Alpheus aged just 8, not only got into the fire he also got himself into a local pond. Walter who was extremely depressed was recorded as having taken carbolic acid. One of the most common choices to end a life was with a knife. Charles [3] admitted with primary dementia at the age of thirteen had taken this choice:–

> *'Says he is always worrying about having knocked a woman on the head with some boards he was carrying, that it has got on his nerves, that he has tried to cut his throat. Very frightened if left alone. Not a second of the day but what he is worrying gets excited when having his meals. Says he keeps looking at his chest to see if one side of him is getting thinner than the other; afraid he is going to die… He has had a cousin on the mother's side who committed suicide and his father has been a drunkard all his life.'*

Young Mary Ann [1] a domestic servant from Overseal near Ashby who was admitted with simple mania –'…was restless and excited at first, talking incessantly, singing and shouting saying she would make away with herself'. William Christmas who had previously been employed as a pageboy, could only give a trivial reason for taking poison (atropine and cocaine) before his admission, but threatened to take it again if he was sent to an asylum. There were the tragic admission records for fourteen–year–old Maria [2], whose behavioural pattern was suspected to have been a result of her being admitted to a Union Workhouse. Her somewhat wild actions placed her in immense danger:–

> *This is a case of maniacal excitement, of a chronic character, which has been in existence some years in a subdued form, but latterly has been called into a more active form in consequence of a sudden constitutional change, the Patients conduct has been very eccentric and irrational creeping through inconceivably small apertures, secreting herself in the most unheard of places, thereby causing much anxiety, she has also manifested very dangerous propensities to herself, and others, throwing herself out of windows, jumping into pits, and exposing herself and others to frequent peril'.*

Henry [1] who had been admitted after stabbing his mother became quite depressed after being a patient for four months:–

> *'A few days ago he lay in bed for a day, said he wanted to go to heaven and not to live.'*

When and where previously under care and treatment as a lunatic, idiot or person of unsound mind

Another enquiry to be completed was as to whether the new incoming patient had previously been under care and treatment as a 'lunatic', 'idiot' or 'person of unsound mind.' This enquiry enlightens any researcher as to the virtual non–existence of any other existing location that could assist in the care of problematic youngsters. It was nearly always blank, or filled with the words 'no', 'not before', 'no where' or 'not previously'. Parents must have had to desperately try and cope with extreme behaviours or concerns. Just 4 out of 135 young admissions had received treatment somewhere else. Both Naomi Millicent and Stanley William had been resident at the Midland Counties Asylum for children, in Knowle near Birmingham. John William [4] had been in a home for boys in Uxbridge. George [2] admitted in December 1849 was recorded to have 'been confined for some time past in Camberwell Asylum.'

Whether any near relative has been afflicted with insanity

Following the section on details of any previous treatment was the query of as to whether there were any hereditary influences to their mental condition.

> *'....from the means adopted her complaint has been relieved, but the hereditary tendency to disease precludes all chance of recovery'. Elizabeth Mary*

Had any other members of the patient's family been afflicted with mental handicap or mental illness? The hereditary query sections were one of the most likely to be blank or the words 'not known', 'none' or 'no' is entered. When parents had actually died, obtaining any family history of illness, would of course be far more problematic. About 20% of the young admissions had other relatives noted, for also experiencing mental problems of some form.

The mentally ill young ones, just like those who were mentally handicapped, had many hereditary factors included within their records. . If it was not actual parents with a history of mental illness, then it would be brothers, sisters, grandparents, uncles, aunts or cousins. The asylum medical men appeared far more confident in their diagnosis of mental insanity if there was knowledge of another family member being likewise afflicted. For many the 'it is not known whether any relatives were similarly afflicted' was dutifully recorded. The historical health and hereditary records for Archibald are very precise:–

> *'No history of neurosis in the family, nor of any maternal impression or accident before birth'.*

Others are less fortunate in their family histories; Charles [3] with primary dementia was recorded to have a cousin who had tragically committed suicide. Frederick [1] with 'simple mania', William Christmas with 'melancholia and Charles [2] with 'dementia' all had relatives who had been mentally ill or had actually died in the asylum. For Albert Isaac his mother had once been a patient in Berrywood Asylum in Northamptonshire, suffering from 'puerperal mania'. For Ida Winifred the words 'a distant relation of her mother's had been mentally afflicted years back' was noted on her reception order. In the case of illegitimacy, to take John [1] as one example, it was often the father's side that took the blame where there was genuinely believed to be some history of insanity, if there was no history of any affliction on the mother's side. John William [4] and Sarah Susan Ravina both had fathers who had been mentally ill.

The most accurate evidence for mental problems running within a family was when more than one family member with mental handicap or illness was admitted to an asylum. Elizabeth [2] had a brother named Henry [3], admitted 3 years later to join her. There was also another 'idiot' brother in the family who was still at home with his father in Kirby Muxloe. Reginald William had a brother Stanley William in the asylum with him. Edward had a sister Ruth in the asylum. For Mary [1] admitted suffering from 'imbecility', the records stated that – 'The other children of the family are well and normally intelligent.'

Two of the enquiries of prime importance were related to alcohol consumption and the infectious lung conditions of their blood relatives. It is interesting that the medical men on admission gave considerable weight to the drinking habits of family members, and the effect this may have had on their offspring. Did they believe that alcohol played that big a part within the onset of both mental handicap and mental illness? James aged just 12 was actually recorded as having no alcoholic history and William [9] was perhaps unnecessarily recorded at the young age of 11 to be 'of temperate habits.' It was usually the parents who were recorded with a history of intemperance. Frederick's [1] father had one of the most defamatory write–ups.

> *'His father was a soldier and died 7 months ago: he is said to have been of very intemperate habits and when in drink was violent and almost maniacal'.*

Cecil's mother suffered a similar fate within the asylum recording system, even though it was not necessarily a personal negativity related purely to alcohol:–

> *'Mother is an unmarried woman of dissolute character'.*

Another important inclusion was whether any of the newcomer's relatives had an infectious lung disease, which was usually given the medical term of 'phthisis'. These infectious lung conditions were rife on both sides of the asylum walls. William [9] had one of the most tragic entries in this section of his records as both his mother, brothers and sisters had all died from consumption.

Supposed cause

It was also necessary to infill whether there was any definite assigned physical cause for their condition. This was one of the sections, for the young ones, where there were frequently blanks or 'not known' was entered. Quite a few have epilepsy or infantile convulsions entered as the physical cause. As for the duration of attack the term 'congenital' is yet again endemic in this section. John Alpheus's entry was even more medically specific 'Disease of the brain – Congenital'. Albert Isaac had severe illness as a baby. Thomas [6] had suffered a more serious accident, when he had been run over at the age of 8 in 1904. For a few of the teenagers it was definitely believed to be their actual age that had caused the onset of mental illness. For Mary Ann [1] with simple mania 'puberty' is entered. With William Christmas his cause is 'adolescence' and for Mary [3] with sub–acute mania it was her 'time of life'.

The reason for the condition for some was far too lengthy to be entered in a relatively small space. Mabel's mother had a serious fright in the third month of her pregnancy. The 11 year old idiot Naomi Millicent, had the onset of her condition suspected to be 'due to injuries to the head at birth (instruments?) in 1891.'

Elsie Matilda had been a premature baby, born at 7 months gestation in 1893.

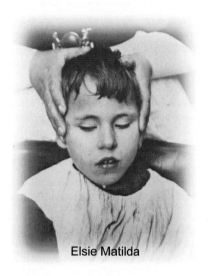

Elsie Matilda

The following entry gives details of what happened to Emily's [2] mother during her pregnancy:–

> *'It appears from the history of this patient her mother when pregnant with her received a fright occasioned by a team of horses passing the door, one of which suddenly began prancing and kicked the waggoner most violently on the bowels to which he immediately applied his hand and exclaimed 'Oh God I am dying'. The poor woman said she never was well after this occurrence and there is no doubt it was the shock to her nervous system so suddenly received that excited such a baneful influence on her progeny'.*

A few of the young ones 'supposed cause' for onset of their mental condition was not purely clinical. Five of those being admitted had had serious injuries to the head due to falls, not all of these accidents resulted in the onset of epilepsy. Samuel was only three months old when this had happened to him.

Readmissions

A high proportion of patients, of every age group, had the good fortune to return home again to familiar faces: A few of every age group, were unfortunately due to suffer remissions, resulting in them having to return to the same or another asylum. Mary Ann [1] a domestic servant and factory hand from Overseal, with simple mania, was the juvenile who experienced the greatest number of readmissions. She was admitted four times in all, but was eventually released recovered in May 1896. Poor Frederick [1] a young biscuit maker who had been blighted by a bad attack of sunstroke in his youth was another of the few young readmissions, being readmitted 3 times. He used to be able to go for walks around the grounds and to go to many of the entertainments, but he also frequently asked to be allowed to go home. When his thoughts became more rational again, he was allowed home eventually forever. This number of repeat admissions was unusual, as only a handful of young patients were actually readmitted.

Just 4 'idiots' or 'imbeciles' were found to have experienced a readmission within their case book records:–

John Samuel Clifford aged 6 on admission was treated for 6 months and readmitted 4 months later and eventually died aged 13 in the Borough Asylum

Samuel was treated for 3 months in 1884 aged 8 and was readmitted at the age of 16 in 1891.

Henry Simon aged 6 received treatment for a year and was readmitted 11 years later .

Arthur [5] aged 10 years received treatment for 6 months and was readmitted 8 years later.

Any other readmissions for those who originally entered at the age of fourteen and under, were for suffering from some form of mental illness, commonly some form of mania.

Walter was readmitted after having been at home again for just under two years. On the second time round, he is recorded as being both extremely depressed and suffering from delusions. His brother an imbecile, had been a great trial to his family, and this had apparently seriously preyed on Walter's mind.

Elizabeth [1] was admitted twice. For the first admission her condition was recorded to be acute mania but for the second admission she was reported to have mental 'imbecility'. Her mother eventually became an inmate with her.

Alfred [1] also had a reclassification of condition - 1st time round he was classified as an 'imbecile' - 2nd times round he was suffering from mania.

Emma [2] with epileptic mania who was removed from the asylum due to problems with the payment of her fees – 4s 6d per week, was readmitted five months later:–

> *'Since her removal, for she has been kept in a dark cellar, chained to a post - the fear and tenor of the neighbourhood'.*

Exceptionally bad behaviour after relocation from an asylum to a Union House led to readmissions.

> *'Since her discharge from the asylum in January of the present year she has been an inmate of the Union House where her conduct has been marked by great violence and intemperate language. Before her admission her conduct was at times gross and indecent and she was therefore sent here by the express authority of the guardians'. Maria* [2]

William Christmas pictured below was a patient at all three Leicestershire Asylums. He was initially admitted to the Borough Asylum, but his admission to the 1st County Asylum near to its closure would have necessitated his relocation to the newly built 2nd County Asylum. His eventual recovery must have been long lasting, as he is eventually recorded as dying aged 78 in Redbridge London.

William Christmas

There are those who may feel that these youngsters had just been 'put away' in the asylum. If this was actually the case, then an incredible amount of detailed observations and official paperwork went into these infantile admissions. After completing any preliminary details taken from reception order certificates or accompanying adults the medical officers were then ready to make their own exceptionally detailed assessments of the new young patients.

Internal Observations and Assessments

The Medical Officer at the time of admission did not solely rely on the information from others. As a man with high medical qualifications he also made his own detailed observations on the youngsters. His assessments appear to be equally focused on both the normalities and abnormalities. The dedicated purpose of his recording was to make if possible, the future treatment of a new patient more effective. The treatment required diagnoses to be made and some of the irrationality portrayed made this task very problematical.

> *'Accurate examination and diagnosis is impossible as he is too idiotic to give any assistance'. William* [5]

The incoming patients were being admitted due to pre–diagnosed mental problems caused by congenital defect, infection, accident, epilepsy, traumatic events or reasons otherwise completely unknown. The nature of some of the entries is quite personalised and it is therefore assumed that the assessors may usually have written directly into the casebooks themselves and did not perhaps have a copy clerk to enter information following the examination.

Any observations and assessments he made were recorded after the initial entry information. There was no separate ledger for this purpose.

Clothing and General appearance

Just about everything that met the 'MO's eyes was recorded. One of the perhaps least important pieces of information he dealt with, was how the youngsters were dressed. A far higher percentage of adults had their clothes commented on at the time of their admission, but this was probably because they were mostly able to choose for themselves how they were dressed. So many aged under fourteen, were noted to destroy their bedding and clothing – like Elizabeth Mary:–

> *'The perfect fiend destroying anything she could lay her hands on'.*

John William [2] had:–

> *Both hands were tied up in mittens which when mother removed he immediately began to bite and tear with his teeth'.*

Those responsible for the appearance on arrival of the new admissions, obviously took the task quite seriously- Emily [2] from East Norton must have been specially prepared for her entry, by family or friends:–

John William [2]

> *'Being perfectly idiotic without possessing even the power of comparison - she was neatly dressed and remarkably clean in her person, but evidently in a very debilitated state of health'.*

Detailed observations were of course not just made of juvenile's clothes at the time of admission. They were arriving from each and every background or location. The asylum staff would hopefully have greeted the rather unkempt and those with dirty hair full of vermin – lice and ticks as warmly as those dressed in a clean condition. There were other unclean, unfortunate infections to be picked up, with for example one girl having tape worm and young boy having ring worms upon his face.

The basic details of appearance were perhaps slightly easier to complete, than more complex medical details, with such items as the colour of hair, eyes and complexion be it pale, ruddy or clear olive (Emily [11]). A pale facial colour was often due to anaemia, as was the case for Willie. One girl was recorded as being both anaemic, and with feeble circulation too.

General bodily health

It was a complete medical appraisal that the 'MO' was recording, as the asylum was also functioning as a hospital. One twelve year old was quite seriously ill at the time of admission. Her health had deteriorated so dramatically, that she had been placed in the local workhouse. She was admitted 31st December 1896; five weeks later she died at the 1st County Asylum from tubercular meningitis. Fortunately, Elizabeth [3] had been admitted to a hospital where she received a high standard of care. This girl was the exception and quite a few of the new incoming young patients were fortunately, physically fine. The most common negativity, with regard to an individual's general health was the use of the adjectives, 'feeble' or 'delicate'.

One of the immediate basic enquiries was to discover how good a young person's appetite was. For some it was 'regular' for some it was 'fair', for some it was 'voracious' and for one with 'thick springy gums', it was 'variable'. Diet was often linked to bowel function. One girl's appetite was very bad, even though her bowels were open regularly. One girl's bowels and faeces were 'habitually, obstinately costive' and 'partially formed'.

The case books had a section entitled 'Physical State' which required an accurate, detailed completion[12]:–

---

12   Alfred2 Inclusion on his physical state taken from his case book record DE3533–206–130

General Stature – Height and Weight

During one period of admission many patients have had measurements of their weight and height recorded. Charles [1] for example aged fourteen, was 5 feet tall and weighed 7 stones 2 pounds. Poor William [3] was unfortunately 'too crooked' to have his height recorded.

Incoming patients were tall, well developed, stout and well made, well nourished, plump, rather thin, or rather slim. The same William [3] was seen to be a 'little half grown undersized creature', not larger than a child of 7 or 8 even though he was 14. A quick visual assessment of Bertie and John William [4] had them both recorded as being 'stunted in growth'.

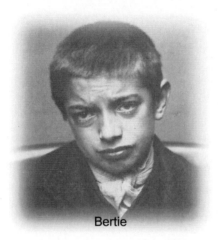

Bertie

One young teenage female was unfortunately written to have:–

A 'body everywhere covered with thick large and rather firm subcutaneous fat'.

With some cases where there were more specific body parts recorded – William [8] was noted to be 'Perfect in corporeal structure and use of limbs'. Sarah Jane had defective gait, with her right foot being in the 'talipes equines position and her right arm was slightly varus and partially paralysed.' Her hand was flexed at her wrist and fingers drawn inward, so that it was unable to grasp. . A tap on his knee had Cecil with his 'patella reflex dulled'. Edith's legs were bowed from rickets, with Betsy having far more serious physical defects as her – 'Left side much paralysed'. Horace had evident spinal curvature, which was written to be slightly increasing during his treatment.

Actual features of head

Not all body parts were on observation, totally satisfactory. Many were admitted with other things very wrong with them, as well as what were considered to be, more temporary or permanent mental defects. One of the most significant body parts to activate a medical, diagnostic comment was quite understandably the head shape. Some were small or microcephalic, whereas others were large, round, square or bullet shaped. Several were quite deformed with 'immense posterior developments' or with 'contractions' in the 'anterior post–positions.' John William [1] had a very large head expanded in the frontal region whereas. Frederick's [3] head was peculiarly formed being compressed laterally. Violet Anne had been hydrocephalic since her birth. Fortunately, the head shape for some young ones was assessed in medical terms as completely normal or 'tolerably well shaped'. Others had their facial features perhaps less appropriately defined within the quest for an accurate record:–

> *This peculiar little creature is almost like one's notion of an 'Aztec'. The head and face are very diminutive and quite colourless - The head measures 17 inches round brows'. Harriett*

> *'Negro like type face, unable to speak, general functions of an animal'. William* [3]

Palate and mouth

Within the skull, is the palate. Many normal palates earned absolutely no comment, but several youngsters had anomalies within their palates recorded. Frederick [3] who was profoundly handicapped had a palate that was very malformed, whereas others were slight, narrow or very arched. Alfred [2] had no uvula to his palate and his nose was so flattened that he was classified as being a mouth breather. William [5] had an arched palate and his upper jaw also considerably hung over the lower one. John Alpheus's jaw was so projected that he gave 'general type monkeyish grimaces.' Another defect of the mouth was faulty salivation. Several were noted for having little control over their saliva ducts, even though this may have been a defect which was essentially beyond them:–

> *'Allows saliva to dribble from her mouth'.*

> *'A drivelling and dangerous idiot from birth'.*

A clean moist tongue was pleasing, but a coated or furred one was not so good. For some with coated tongues, their breath was noted for being 'foul'. Some teeth were 'perfect' whereas others were 'bad'. One individual, who is recorded with the lateral incisors being pegged and notched, emphasizes the extent of the detailed examinations made in the initial patient assessments.

Heart and Lungs

After the shape of the head came details of circulation and breathing. The circulation of some was feeble. The skin and extremities were touched with some being very cold. Pulses were also felt and readings were taken. Some of these examinations were recorded with pulses being 'quick and wiry', or 'slow and full', 'laboured' or 'quicker than was natural'. Meticulous details were often given with one pulse rate being '88 per minute'. For many the pulse was 'naturally standard'. A couple of youngsters were admitted with very definite problems with their thyroid glands. Sarah Jane, Arthur [1] and Thomas [2] had been noted for a considerable amount of choria (involuntary spasmodic movements). It proved difficult on admission to examine Albert Isaac's lungs, but the left lung was written to have phthisis. Some were recorded as respiration being quicker than normal with Edith's being 'noisy and resembling the forced respiration produced at will by adults. A couple were admitted with a rather worrying cough.

Skin condition

There were also problems either with
skin conditions or with marks on their
skin from various wounds Elizabeth [1]
and George [3] both had faces covered
with acne spots and the medical officer
had quickly drawn a sketch of George's [3]
face and the spots.[13]

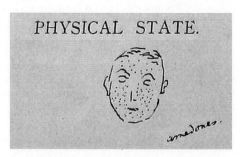

Another teenager named Arthur [1] had a face that looked as if it was burning hot all over
due to:–

> *'Congenital capillary naevus, the same affection is found in patches on his
> gluteal regions, legs and arms and partly on the chest'.*

One boy had several small ulcers on his front left leg and another boy had a scar from
an abscess. Many of those who were afflicted with epilepsy had several wounds, due to
falling, during convulsions. George [2] had a scar on his right eyebrow, which was the
result of a fall in a fit. John Samuel Clifford had a haematoma from an accidental fall
and Fred had two marks of burns on the inner side of his left arm and in front of his
left elbow.

General mobility

The two most important tasks for the doctor on admission, was to assess the general
mobility skills and mental capacities. It was far easier for the doctors to visually gauge
an individual patient's physical abilities, than it was to assess their cognitive skills.
Fortunately, the majority had absolutely no mention of mobility problems. There are
a small number of entries where their 'gait' is mentioned but it is recorded with such
phrases as 'free from clumsiness', 'unimpaired', or 'perfect'.

Those with the most severe defects within their mobility, were usually those who were
also diagnosed to be 'idiots' or 'imbeciles' Elizabeth Mary was described as follows:–

> *'She is an active lively creature but totally devoid of intellectuality'.*

George [6] was noted as:–

> *'Betrays his defective development in his clumsy and lumpish gait and thick
> awkward lower limbs'.*

At least George [6] was privileged with mobility, even if it was impaired. Several of the
young 'idiots' like Lily were essentially immobile, recorded as always sitting 'in a low
chair and being practically helpless in it'. It is not clear now severe Joseph Montague's

---

13   George[3] Case Book Page DE3533–197–4748 Photograph Courtesy of the Record Office for Leicestershire, Leicester and
Rutland

physical difficulties were and if he too was spending his days in a chair (which was sometimes carried out into the sunshine) but he was unable to stand. A handful were noted as never having been able to walk or stride out independently and one young man named John Samuel Clifford had only taken his first steps at the age of four. A couple of the young walkers were described as 'tottering' about. Some were far more severely physically afflicted. Edgar William suffered right–sided infantile hemiplegia with the arm being worse than his leg. Mary [2] was occasionally afflicted with partial hemiplegia. A handful were recorded with some degree of paralysis. Betsy was 'much paralysed left side' and Emily [2] when examined was diagnosed as having many of the symptoms of general paralysis. This specific condition was usually acquired through contracting syphilis and infected parents could pass it on to their unborn child.

Assessment of Mental Skills

Assessing locomotive skills could be accomplished visually: Assessing mental capacity was a far more formidable task. At times it seems that it was purely the incoming patients' appearance that led to the allocation of a more specific condition within learning disability. The medical officers had perhaps already decided what an 'idiot' should look like – 'He has the characteristic appearance of an idiot' – 'Is idiotic in appearance'. – 'Idiotic expression of countenance'.

> *The expression of the countenance, though constantly smiling is perfectly idiotic without a spark of intelligence - There was nothing what ever to be done in this case, unfortunately the patient being dangerous idiot and consequently incurable'. Emily* [2]

Mary Ann [2] on the other hand had a 'very imbecilic expression of countenance'. With Arthur [4] though there 'was nothing in his face or form to agree with his congenital 'idiocy'. Similarly, Maria Martha also appeared 'to have an intelligent expression far beyond her mental capacity'. Actual age may have had some influence on the decision as to a young one's mental capacity. The average age for an under fourteen year old classified as an 'idiot', was 9: The average age for those classified as 'imbeciles' was 11. There was a tendency for the 'idiots' to be admitted at a far younger age and all the 3 and 4 year olds, were so classified at the time of their admission.

At times there were interesting observations made at the time of the initial assessment as was the case for George [2]:–

> *This is a case of epileptic mania, which came on about six years ago - the patient's natural disposition seems most amiable - in point of mind he seems perfectly 'imbecile'.*

One of the newcomers with completely contradictory appraisals is Emily [1] a foundling aged just 10 – her records state 'This child is undoubtedly a dumb idiot' but her final diagnosis for admission was 'imbecile'. The earliest records for Eunice state –

> *'She is quite an imbecile and talks very peculiarly and cannot be understood. She shouts and makes a great noise, sings suddenly changes and becomes violent. She has fits occasionally'.*

Just two rows of script away under 'Symptoms of Mental Disorder' she is recorded as having 'epileptic idiocy'– Young Henry [3] from Kirby Muxloe with a sister and brother also both 'idiots', was noted to have a severe degree of 'idiocy', but there was no further information to back up the reason for the use of the adjective 'severe'. The initial diagnosis was occasionally queried later on within an individual's treatment period:–

> *'Has more intelligence than she was at first accredited with. Likes to go to the dances and entertainments and is disappointed if she does not go'. Ida Winifred December 1904*

There was also Elsie aged just ten when she was recorded as an 'idiot':–

> *'She was when not shy inclined to talk quite intelligently, can count her fingers and the number of buttons on the nurses dress up to eleven. Observes and is interested in pictures, her manners are good in asking or receiving anything. Is backward in intelligence for her age'.*

One of the Asylum Medical Officers tasks was to try to assess his new young patients' attention skills. With young Alfred [2], who appeared to exhibit the usual signs of 'idiocy'–

> *'It is possible to attract his attention, but impossible to sustain it for any length of time'.*

Communication and Interaction

An individual's attention skills obviously had an influence on their ability to interact with others and to communicate successfully. Many had been unable to talk or to use intelligible sounds. Tragically, at times the only interactions initially offered by the young patients were recorded as noise.

> *'This idiot boy is prone to shout aloud without apparent cause - emitting a loud discordant cry'. William [3] 1880 March 25th*

It was though quite worrying when there was no vocal interaction whatsoever from several of the youngsters:–

> *'Has not uttered a sound since admission'. Ethela Isola*

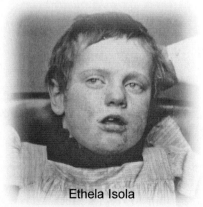

A few others are recorded as having never spoken. At times record was made of successful communication by gestures, such as 'a nod of the head'. A patient's hearing skills were always tested, this was particularly relevant if communication skills were poor. The 'dumb' had to be tested to see if they were both 'deaf and dumb'. William [5]:–

> *'Could not speak but his hearing was distinct'.*

Ethela Isola

A few only had one or two spoken words and these were usually the names of their closest relatives, – 'Mamma', 'Dada' or 'Papa' – to whom they were effectively not going to have the language skills to be able to soon say goodbye to.

A few were unable to answer questions or any language used was exceptionally incoherent. Archibald was recorded with some speech but it was exceptionally limited when compared to a normal child of the same age.

'Is very lively and playful, makes monosyllabic demands 'cheese', 'orange', 'band', 'soldiers' – rarely strings more than 2 or 3 words together'.

Some like Archibald who had just a few words, would pronounce them very imperfectly. A small number, who could speak, would understandably have speech defects. William [4] and Sarah would both stammer and Harriett articulated 'some single words very oddly.' Sarah Jane exhibited quite defective pronunciation of several words:–

Archibald

'girl' is 'dell – joiner is flower – dead is bread'.

Horace would make sounds chiefly commencing with labials (b and d) such as 'bill–bill' and 'dada'.

There is one very profoundly, multiply handicapped young lad named Frederick [3] who was never classified as an 'idiot' he was always an 'imbecile'.

'This is a case of mental imbecility, which has existed from birth. The patient is completely unable either to walk, speak or feed himself. He is obliged to be fed with a spoon of the attendant and he passes faces and urine apparently without consciousness. He is almost continually making a peculiar muttering sound with the mouth, which becomes more marked when he is in any way excited and seems most so when he suffers from cold of which he has great intolerance. He is usually seen sucking his fingers of which process they show the mark. He spends the day swaying to and fro and making guttural sounds from time to time'.

Exceptionally poor communication skills usually resulted in the term 'idiot' being the label for an individual.

Assessment of General Levels of Intelligence

One of the most strategic investigations was to try and ascertain the levels of intelligence of a young newcomer to the asylum. Young Alfred [3] admitted at the age of 7 in 1876 with epileptic mania following sunstroke, had his levels of intelligence assessed in quite an unusual way:–

> *'He seems an intelligent enough lad although he exhibits no surprise or disgust in being in an asylum'.*

An 'imbecile' named Annie 'had not much mind': An 'idiot' named Olive 'had not much sense'. Willie had very basic levels of intelligence – 'Knows his name and smiles when spoken to'. Sarah was an 'imbecile' of severe degree who was 'regardless of heat or cold and had no healthy evolution of mind'. Frances Anne Elizabeth had no idea of time, 'not knowing if it was summer or winter'. In August 1902. William [8] who was congenitally weak minded; when questions were asked of him, he would 'sometimes answer them correctly, but would more frequently get them wrong'. He was also noted to not know the name of his father. Arthur [2] an epileptic 'imbecile' was 'unable to recognise the same person on consecutive days'. Sarah Elizabeth admitted in 1869 from Havelock Street in Leicester was recorded with an additional problem with her imbecility:–

> *'Her intellect does not seem to have received any culture'.*

The doctor on admission often used basic alphabetical or simple numeric tasks as a fundamental part of his initial assessment, on those that had the language skills to be able answer. The following case book entries give some insight into some of the initial assessments that were made on the incoming youngsters:–

a) 'Can count up to 10 after that is lost and says the first few numbers indiscriminately– cannot add 1 and 2 – asked if given 2 apples now and 2 minutes after how many would she have replied "I'd eat half of it" and laughed'. Sarah Jane

b) 'He does not know the first letter of the alphabet, though he can write his name, can count up a few simple figures, is inclined to repeat the same answer to different questions'. – Arthur [1]

c) 'He seems to know very little, can count a little and says his alphabet correctly but cannot spell a word'. Walter

d) 'He could not tell me the names of the months and said there were seven for one year. He also said there were seven pennies for one shilling in a pound and was unable to give me answers to other simple questions'. Thomas [5]

e) 'Patient is well mannered, clean, and alert and shows little mental; abnormality until his education is brought into question. He knows the letters and figures but cannot read the simplest word. He cannot name the different coins with any certainty, knows the common flowers'. John William [4]

f) 'Asked how old he is, says he is going by train'. William [6]

Another vital part of the initial assessment would be a detailed observation of any behaviour. In John William's [3] case his idiocy was only confirmed by his actual behaviour and nothing else. Elizabeth Mary was 'an active lively little creature, but totally devoid of intellectually'. One of the most basic and clearest modes of assessment was to judge whether the newcomers were able to act their age.:–

> *'Does everything in a very babyish way, pleased with babyish things, her actions are aimless'.. Ethela Isola*

Albert was:–

> *'Quite unable to occupy himself as a boy of his age naturally would'.*

Horace:–

> *'Ran about in an aimless fashion making peculiar noises, instead of talking. He played with straws or pieces of paper hitting the wall with them'.*

The Medical Officers decided that there was no method in his play and that it was not the play of a child.

Many of the diagnostic inclusions related to behaviour within the casebook records, are painfully negative–

> *'No signs of any dawning intelligence'. Hilda*

> *'Practically no sense'. Olive*

> *'No intelligence can be obtained – idiot'. Reginald William*

> *'He makes more or less playful attempts to hit anyone he is with, but on the whole is inclined to be friendly so far as he is capable of showing any feeling'. Frederick* [2]

> *'The faculties have never developed'. William* [5]

> *'In fact a drivelling and dangerous idiot from birth. – He does not appear to possess memory and understanding'. John* [1]

> *'Is devoid of affection for his parents or any one else, plays in a silly fashion and makes no request to go home'. George Henry*

> *'Has a congenital inability to distinguish between right and wrong. I shall class him as Congenitally Deficient in mind'. – Edmund*

There are some slightly questionable entries – could anybody who exhibited a considerable amount of cunning, be devoid of intelligence? Edith for example in April 1890 showed considerable intelligence when she wanted to express her own way. '

The Asylum doctor's assessment of those aged fourteen and under who were mentally ill, was far more within his usual diagnostic procedures. Some inclusions from the admission records of the young mentally ill suffering from dementia, melancholia and acute, sub–acute, chronic and epileptic mania are quite comparable to the entries for the far older mentally ill admissions:–

a) Thomas [2] – Chronic Mania – 'This is a case of chronic mania, the boy is unable to answer a simple question at all correctly. He is always in mischief purloining any portable thing within his reach – He seems quite unable to understand the slightest thing'.

b) Mary Ann [1] – Simple mania – 'She seems excited at a very little and while answering questions put to her, without hesitation she will ramble. She is short and child like in form – Says she had been making something in the frying pan but the dog would not eat it'.

c) Frederick [1] – Simple mania – 'Patient throws himself about taking no notice of what is said to him. Constantly rambling about Jack the Ripper'.

d) Charles [2] – Dementia – 'Suffers from delusions – At times he does not know that he is at home and fails to recognise his mother'.

e) Charles [3] – Primary dementia – 'Nervous and confused. He tells me he thinks he grows too much every day and that his heart beats too much'.

f) Walter – Mania – 'On admission responds quickly to questions and answers them well. Collects bits of paper because they are following him. Points to imaginary objects on the floor. Although he reads well he cannot multiply simple numbers'.

g) Elizabeth [1] – 'Acute mania with great feebleness of mental power during the intervals of tranquillity. She has also some delusions'.

h) Mary [3] – Sub–acute mania. – 'The patient was very noisy in her conversation which was at the same time quite rambling and unconnected'.

i) Alfred [1] – Mania – 'Is very rambling and incoherent in speech and often sings his remarks' e.g. 'Have a rattle' – 'Come on Lancashire' – 'Its down in Northamptonshire' – 'We'll all be merry drinking, whisky, wine and sherry, there they come – there they come – dead men.' – 'Its meat and potato pie tomorrow'.

For some who were more fortunate, on very rare occasions 'normality' was the eventual diagnosis. For Charles [2] initially classified with 'dementia' there is the following entry just a month after admission:–

'Is mentally rational, bright cheerful and industrious and beyond a little confusion on admission has really shown no signs of mental aberration'.

It is very evident from the records, that patients at the time of their admission were all given both a very thorough medical examination plus an assessment of their mental health and cognitive abilities.

Charles [2]

The People in the Asylum

Any under fourteen year old would require some degree of guidance and care from an adult regardless of whether they were 'sane', 'insane' or 'person of unsound mind'. Once the young patients were admitted with a Reception Order Certificate, there would be two sets of adults within their lives – their family and friends or the asylum staff. Admission to an asylum would take the young ones away from the normality of their former lifestyles.

There were just a handful of young patients who potentially had regular access to both a parent and staff, as one of their parents was actually receiving treatment with them. There is though no information as to whether they were being cared for in close proximity to one another, or in the same ward for example. Mary Ann [2] and her mother Ann were admitted together on the same day, but her mother took little notice of her, probably because she was seriously mentally ill herself with chronic mania. It was 6 years before Elizabeth's [4] mother Rachel, also an imbecile, joined her, also from Lutterworth Union House – She would have nothing at all to do with her mother. Another, Elizabeth's [1] mother, also joined her from home after 7 years.

It is unfair to try and judge how much the parents missed their children following admission. Many of the young ones, especially those who were designated to be 'idiot' or 'imbecile' patients appear essentially to become no longer an integral part of their relatives lives. Ethela Isola was admitted at the age of 7 from Langham, Oakham in 1907. Two years later she was dead from pneumonia and tragically written diagonally across her name in red ink were the words 'We to bury'. This may not though have been lack of affection, as for many parents, these were hard times and lack of funding may also have initiated this sad occurrence.

Alternately, it is impossible to assess or judge how much the patients missed their homes and close relatives. After his admission the illegitimate infant Cecil William had only been heard to mutter one word –"Mamma." Another lad named William [6]:–

> *'He cannot answer a question rationally and in reply to most questions he either whistles or calls out Mamma'.*

Albert Isaac called everyone 'Daddy'. A few like Walter, Frances Anne Elizabeth and William [6] are recorded as crying or fretting for one of their parents. Some were less distressed, but it was still very evident where perhaps they would rather be. Frederick [1] asked to go home, Mary Elizabeth at times asked for her mother, but she did not cry if she did not come to see her. Elizabeth [1] was smitten with a delusion that she could hear her mother calling her. Thomas's [6] records are quite daunting to read. He was admitted to the asylum after spending 3 years in the Loughborough Union. His father at the time of his asylum admission was at their home. The following are various extracted entries from his case book entries. It appears that he was missing both his family and home:–

1888 April 5th 'Writes letters home and seems contented where he is.'

1888 Oct 22nd 'While out at work today on the farm he absconded about lunch time.'

1888 Oct 28th 'Was brought back again today from Loughborough. He had sold his clothes and boots and came in very ragged garments. Had large blisters on both heels from tramping about the country and looked worn out and rather stupid.'

1896 Jan 27th 'Always wants to write letters, most of his return by dead letter office: he is moved by religions'.

The young ones were essentially taken away from their previous carers, which were usually their parents and less frequently the residential officials of workhouses. Before any patient was going to return to their lives on the other side of the walls they had to be reasonably physically well and their behaviours had to be generally socially acceptable again. The long–standing priority was to get patients of any age well again, or to get them so relieved that they could be classified as 'sane' again.

Within the asylum they would be in the company of other adults, the staff of the asylum, plus patients too. Details were rarely if ever given, as to which ward a patient was placed. The exception was the multiply frail or the very young new infant male admissions, who were placed in the female wards, to be cared for by some of the female adult patients, which was particularly those women who were not well enough to work outside the ward complex.

The delicate state of this boy's health is such that he was placed in the Female Ward no 1 for a short period. He became an occupational task for the female mentally ill patients'. James [3]

These allocations of young males like William [2] and Horace to a female ward would result in a double care system from both staff and patients coming into operation. Female patients without their own offspring could of course have very willingly become much needed substitute mothers. The young inmates inadvertently became something to do for the older patients.

Strong maternal instincts were therefore given a direct occupational focus as some adult female patients were often missing their own sons and daughters. They quite naturally and voluntarily cared for the young on their ward. They were not just opportunities to care; they were also great company. Before the era of the modern day technologies, the young ones like Maria Martha could be a great source of amusement for some of the old women in the ward. Young Horace and Emily [1] were both quite well behaved and much feted by the female patients.

The younger age group would of course have benefited from the company of their own age groups. Fortunately, when admission dates are compared, it is evident that there was regularly the chance for the new arrivals to be in the company of someone of a similar age and sex. Mary [2] from East Norton was lucky that, 'There is another little girl about her size who makes a good play fellow for her'. Below are a few examples of other young ones of similar ages being resident at the same time: –

Arthur [4] aged 4 and John William [3] aged 5 admitted 2 months apart to County 1877

Elsie aged 9 and Naomi aged 11 admitted a fortnight a part 1902

Duncan aged 6, Albert aged 9, Edgar William aged 8, John Samuel Clifford aged 6 were admitted between 1903–1904

George [5] aged 13 and Albert aged 13 admitted 1905

Muriel Gertrude aged 10 and Elsie aged 10 admitted 1908

The loss of daily contact with their families, or their 'friends', must have inevitably encouraged building relationships within the asylum. Some had such warm personalities that making acquaintances was quite easily enabled. For example, when fourteen year old George [2] was admitted with epileptic mania, his manners were so winning, that he became a great favourite with all his fellow patients in his ward. The asylums ran far more smoothly if the patients of any age could build good relationships with one another. Even an 'idiot' named Edward developed strong working relationships with other patients of similar mental abilities:–

'…..appears to vie with other idiots in the ward in strange antics.'

Through their admission to an asylum in Leicestershire, the longer–stay patients became members of another family. There was a home family meal table: There was the asylum family meal table too. Communicative interaction was always more evident if any food was involved. The loosening of relational bonds for those not quickly recovered or released back home must have inevitably resulted in fellow patients or staff, becoming their more familiar face instead. Meaningful reactions developed regardless of an individual's level of intelligence. The initial potential negativities, towards what must have been somewhat anomalous appearances, would have faded, as the young individuals became a familiar, recognisable face with a name.

The asylum staff's sole, primary and waged occupation was to care for and nurture recovery of their patients. For the carers at home, the very necessary care and watchfulness, required to maintain reasonable levels of safety, would often take them away from their professions that financed family life, or the prime household tasks that were necessary to manage a happy home. The twenty–four hour, hyper–demanding child–minding commitments, borne out of catering for those with severe learning difficulty, were often way beyond the average family care experiences.

Unmanageable behaviours or worrying conditions such as severe epileptic mania eventually resulted in strong relationships being formed with the medical officers of the asylums.

'Arthur [2] *frequently declared - 'Good night doctor bless your little heart'.*

John William [4] also gave the doctors special recognition in his own individual manner:–

'Salutes in a respectful way, when one is going through the ward'.

The Asylum records for all the three Leicestershire asylums open the doors to the care that the newly admitted would receive. Within the script of the casebooks, many words did at that time start with a capital letter and a patient was a patient with a capital 'P'. They were very certainly going to be looked after, as in the Matron's duties it is clearly written that:–

'She shall see all the Female patients, and every ward appropriated for their use, at least twice a day'.[14]

Mrs Beaumont Head Nurse 1ˢᵗ County Asylum

The Senior Male Attendant probably had a duty to follow similar watchful guidelines. There are also constant inclusions within the Superintendents' Journals for visits of the outsiders, the Official Guardians from various settlement areas, coming in observe patients from their settlement areas. Within many thousand sheets of paperwork there are very few negative inclusions as to their actual care.

The main carers would be keepers, attendants and nurses who worked under the leadership of the superintendent, doctors, matron and chief attendant. There were also many other staff such as the cooks, various maids, skilled individuals in the training workshops, gardeners and workers on the farms, with whom patients would regularly interact. The employees of the asylum generally would just live in just like the patients.

14   Photograph of Mrs Beaumont Head Nurse – Stewart Collection Leicestershire County Record Office

In 1897 the staffing numbers were as follows:–

1 Head Attendant (Male)

1 Head Nurse (Female)

For days 20 men and 24 women, giving a ratio of one attendant to eleven inmates on each side.

For Nights: 3 men and 3 women[15]

These asylum staff certainly knew their place. The architectural plans for the 2nd County Asylum show that all the staff were quite specifically arranged with offices and rooms in various locations, which was dependent on their professional status. The medical officers, assistant medical officers, matron, assistant matron, cook, chaplain and clerk all had their own offices. The officers also had their own day rooms and dining rooms.

Dr Rothsay C Stewart
Stewart Collection – Photograph courtesy of the Record Office for
Leicestershire, Leicester & Rutland.

15   Leicestershire's Lunatics – The Institutional care of Leicestershire's Lunatics during the Nineteenth Century H G Orme W H Brock Leicestershire Museums and Art Galleries 1987 ISBN 085022 227 3

With the attendants and nurses also having these rooms too. The servants had a hall with the laundry maids being noted for having their own dining room. Even the attendant's and nurses bicycles had to be kept in completely separate areas. Jobs in the asylum appear to have been well sought after for in February 1875, 48 youths applied for the office of steward's assistant and of this number, twenty–three made formal application for the situation.[16] The Superintendents and their staff were very particular about who they chose to have working in their establishment.

Dr Rothsay Stewart,[17] a superintendent at both of the County Asylums was quite a renowned figure. In August 1909 he was appointed by the Medico Psychological Association of Great Britain as a delegate to attend the International Medical Congress in Budapest. He kept himself up to date with absolutely everything from the new availability of corned beef; to modern approaches within asylum architecture. In 1912 he inspected the verandas and method of treating the patients in the open air at the Burntwood and Hatton asylums – 2 years later verandas were erected on the male side of the 2nd County Asylum. It was up to the Superintendents to among other things keep the asylum warm and safe. He investigated the efficiency of latest American stoves.. Within the journals he always signed himself – I am your obedient servant J Rothsay Stewart. If only the patients and staff, could have equalled his own standards of behaviour!

Amongst the original Borough Asylum records at Record Office for Leicestershire, Leicester and Rutland is a very informative notebook in which the Superintendent or another strategic officer has jotted down short quips of details on individuals who were interested in gaining employment within the establishment. The contents are exceptionally enlightening.[18] There are many comments made on an interested applicant's general appearance. Those who showed themselves to be genuinely keen and anxious to come were of course viewed quite favourably. It appeared to be essential that any prospective newcomer should be tall. Frances was 'too short and not suitable', with Elizabeth in January 1885, being actually stated to be 'half an inch below standard'. Fanny aged 18 in 1891 was one of several thought to be too young and was asked to apply again in 12 months. At the other end of the age spectrum, George Robotham was aged 40 and was suffering from angina. He was considered to be too old for permanent employment. They were though more elderly staff in employment though as in 1851 Joseph an attendant was 62, in 1861 Jane a nurse was 61 and in 1881 James an attendant was 60[19].

Good health was the most important key to the door for asylum employment. Many were noted to be 'likely looking' and anybody accredited with those two words usually had a generally healthy appearance. Mary Jane Lee from Linton, Burton on Trent, was offered the next vacancy if her character was acceptable, as she had had no illness of any kind since her childhood. Information on any previous serious illnesses such as rheumatic fever and diphtheria was given. A couple of new applicants had gastric

16   Superintendent's Journal 1– DE2853–40
17   Photograph of Dr Rothsay C. Stewart one of the former Medical Superintendents Stewart Collection Courtesy of Leicestershire, Leicester and Rutland Record Office
18   DE2853–89 Applications to work at Borough Asylum
19   National Census Records

problems such as constant indigestion or ulcers. Lillian had had anaemia and Mary admitted to coughing just in wintertime. Those who appeared too delicate were usually in consequence declined.

With some of the prospective applicants an individual's hearing skills were also recorded. Myra who had had twelve years experience as a laundress was deaf but reported that it was 'on account of a cold and only temporary'. Robert who was hard of hearing was given a post of a temporary attendant in March 1902. Charlotte was recorded as having 'an impediment in her speech'. Certain applicants were to have had an eye test (Harriett in 1897) or were asked to acquire a medical certificate. It was also beneficial if an individual could seem to be both reasonably refined with a sound degree of intelligence. Isabella and Ethel may have been unsuccessful as one is recorded with 'perspiring feet' and the other with 'bad breath'.

Future staff must have also been given a handwriting task, as Georgina who was applying to be a kitchen maid in 1897 was a 'bad writer'. Some were recorded as bringing very good testimonials with them, but Albert Wright in October 1904 had mislaid his 'parchment'. Previous employers would be written to, usually the next day, to obtain 'characters'. Unfortunately, it was ascertained that an Eliza had 'brought a false character' to the asylum with her, whereas Thomas's reference proved that his conduct was exemplary. Any previous experiences or skills always held any applicant in good stead. For those looking for jobs as keepers, attendants or nurses it was beneficial if they had previous nurse training. Annie Waring enquiring in October 1887 aged 54 for a post of night nurse, had formerly been trained in nursing at Kings College. Not everyone seeking a post had any previous experience or qualifications. One young lady had never been in service before. On August 23rd 1893 Charlotte Wilson applies for laundry place, but has not had much experience. Most of the successful applicants appear to have been given a month's probation in order to prove themselves worthy of an occupation within the asylum. Once they became staff, there probably was a certain amount of in-house training. In the later years, the staff were noted to have gained quite high qualifications. In July 1913 two nurses and one attendant were successful in the Preliminary Examination for the nursing certificate of the Medico Psychological Association held in the previous May.[20]

There were also many inclusions related to other occupations, which helped to gain them employment within the asylum:–

1888 April 10th James Veary 3 children youngest 6. Wife wants to live in Leicester. Is known to French understands plumbing, glazing and painting.

1885 Oct 19th Eliza Bonser can dress make and sew well.

1889 Dec 30th Isaac Carter Understands mattress making and upholstery generally.

1884 Aug James Hazzle understands making and baking cakes, pies and buns

1885 May 16th John Flint – Always used to horses was formerly a farmer

1900 Aug 11th Ernest Harcourt Can mow with a scythe.

1886 April 28th Understands stock as well as garden work.

1892 May 23rd Wm Charles Hardy farmer works with stock can thatch.

1885 April 15th Michael Hill an Irishman can play piccolo and violin.

1901 Oct 7th Alfred Clarke 25 in cycling trade – Willing to stoke and make himself useful in any capacity

One applicant could not start immediately as she was required to give a month's notice. In April 1901 Ernest Timson was in the Reserves, but had not produced his discharge. At times people were enquiring about potential employment when there were not any vacancies. If they were considered to be suitable applicants their name was placed on a list.

As an employee the wages were never very high. Wages are entered on a quarterly basis within the Salaries and Wages Register of the 1st County Asylum.[21] For the quarter ending 29th March 1851, the salaries were as follows:–

The Superintendent £75

The Asylum Matron £13.2.6

The Asylum Chaplain £10

The Asylum Clerk £35.12.6

For 11 Keepers for that quarter the wages ranged from £1.7 to £4.5s. The average wage was approximately £4 a quarter

The 12 nurses wages ranged from 5 shillings (assumedly part–time) to £4. The average wage was approximately £3 15 shillings a quarter

6 Indoor workers salaries ranged from £1.12.6 to £3.5

6 Outdoor workers whose salaries ranged from £3.10 to £9.15

The gardener was paid £3.5.6

On 3rd March 1891 the dedicated Asylum staff make an application for a pay rise. Their last request for more wages had been made 15 years before. In October 1897 the shoemaker with 27 years service and the tailor with 18 both applied for an increase in wages, for the first time. Once they were on the payroll, staff were expected to comply with the high standards of asylum life. Within the Superintendent's Journals there were details, on any significant event involving a member of the asylum staff regardless of their status. There were specific rules to be complied with and disobeying them usually led to loss of leave, to suspension from duty for a couple of weeks or total dismissal

---

21 DE3533–94 Salaries and Wages March 1849–Dec 1862

from their position. The non–compliance with the regulations, led to various interesting inclusions within the still extant Superintendent's Journal's for the 1st and 2nd County Asylums and the Borough Asylum.

There are far more negative entries within the Borough Asylum Journals than the 1st County Asylum. Was this because staff discipline was more lax in one of them? One attendant was dismissed for disobeying orders, with no more details. In 1872 a nurse named Selina was given one month's notice to leave, for refusing to be vaccinated. There was a case noted of special bathing rules being broken, with one member of staff leaving another member alone in a bathroom. Some staff were defined as inefficient with some being suspended, or in more serious cases they were given a month's notice. One of the more frequent faux pas, or a 'gross neglect of duty' was the failure to take sufficient care in accurately counting walking parties on their return, resulting in an escape. Several staff members chose to resign rather than face suspension.

The staff were not allowed to be just anywhere. There were very strict rules on where they could be. In January 1896 one attendant was suspended for being found in the Storekeeper's private sitting room. An entry for June 1896 shows just how particular the Borough Superintendent was about where his staff should be: –

> *'I have given permission for the nurses to go out upon the croquet lawn on certain evenings in the week after duty hours until further notice. This privilege has been granted owing to the crowded state of the female mess room but it is understood that it will be withdrawn should it be abused in any way'.*[22]

One of the most likely causes for dismissal were immoral events. In the County asylum in February 1870, Theodosia a laundry maid and Robert an attendant were both suspended from further service as a consequence of Theodosia being absent from the laundry a great proportion of the night on two nights (there was sleeping accommodation for the laundry staff adjacent to the wash house). In 1885 a male attendant, who was a married man with 3 children, went into the female ward number 3 at about 3.30 am. He appeared to get away with this incident but a senior nurse named Martha lost her job for not reporting the event. In May 1870 a nurse named Ann from the County asylum, had to be suspended in consequence of her being pregnant. In November 1881 a nurse named Sarah (from the Borough Asylum) was eventually sentenced to 14 days imprisonment (without hard labour) at the Assizes for having concealed the birth of her baby. Morals were high and if, as a mess room maid you let a painter put his arm around your waist (in August 1896), then you received a caution and your leave of absence was stopped for a month.

Many of the reasons for severe staff reprimands never affected the patients. There was one form of negative behaviour, which often had to be reported to the Commissioners for Lunacy and this was any case of ill treatment of patients. One attendant was fined £5 including costs, for striking a patient in August 1872. At the 1st County Asylum, two nurses were found to have given a problematic patient several blows to the face; the Superintendent subsequently held an enquiry and censure was passed upon both nurses. In 1879 two Commissioners actually ordered an attendant to be prosecuted for striking a patient named Arthur. There were also various suspensions for not reporting bruises, for rough treatment, for unjustifiable or unnecessary violence or not giving a satisfactory account of how an injury was caused.

The extent of potential danger that the staff were placed in should never be overlooked. On August 26th 1875 John Smith an attendant at the Borough Asylum, was stabbed to death by a patient named George. He was found guilty of 'wilful murder' at his trial at the Castle and was ultimately sentenced to death. December 15th 1875 [23]

One of the most frequent reasons for reprimand was for any unauthorised absence from duty. If you were going out on leave, then you were expected to get permission to do this. Even the Superintendent was also required to give notice of his absences. Some were in trouble for not being present for part of a day, or for leaving early. For others it was a longer absence of two days with the longest recorded non–appearance being nine days. Several members of staff, who had been previously cautioned about any absences without permission, were in serious trouble if this event occurred again.

There are some cases of theft noted. At times it was for stealing patient's property. At the Borough asylum thefts of money, jewellery and other valuable articles had been made from the asylum patient's stores. A county asylum teacloth marked 'M' was found at the residence of an attendant named Joseph and another staff member was dismissed from the Borough for having taken a bar of soap from a drawer in a charge attendant's bedroom. The theft of a purse led to a month's imprisonment with hard labour. A nurse named Sarah also suffered the same fate, as she could not give a satisfactory account of certain articles belonging to a certain patient who had recently died. Even the outdoor staff were kept an eye on and in 1888 a carter was suspended for stealing asylum cabbages.

In addition to the records of the Superintendents, doctors, matrons, attendants and nurses there were also records of the artisans to in the Superintendents Journals. In June 1904 an upholsterer was suspended after having appeared before magistrates in court, when he was ordered to pay half a crown a week towards the maintenance of an illegitimate child.

One of the darkest ways to blacken one's character was to have an inappropriate relationship with alcohol. There are quite a few inclusions in the journals related to incidents of intemperance especially in the Borough Superintendent's Journals. Returning from leave of absence in a state of intoxication was definitely not expected to happen. One employee was suspended on Christmas Day 1888 for being the worse for drink when he was on duty that evening. Staff were even expected to remain sober within the annual celebratory servant's ball (January 1883). An inclusion for Ann in September 1878, emphasizes the fact that for the asylum workers, the work venue had truly become their home:–

'Ann…suspended for coming home intoxicated last evening'.[24]'

23   DE2853–41 Borough Asylum Superintendent's Journal 2
24   DE2853–41 Journal 2 Borough Superintendent's Journal

Several workers were warned, especially if it was just the first offence and had their leave stopped. A more serious consequence of intemperance was to be suspended from service. It was both sexes who committed this offence. One attendant was suspended for bringing in four bottles of beer in July 1885. There were even occasions when the staff, usually attendants who had sent a patient to a public house in New Humberstone, for alcohol in January 1878. Another attendant Thomas induced a patient to bring him in a bottle of whisky in 1881. The Official Visitors who also kept a regular inspective check on the asylum and its running, had to report on Burton a porter, who had been found drunk after a Harvest Festival one evening. He had also been severely reprimanded some two months before, for being drunk at Newtown Unthank Farm, during the official visit of the House Committee.[25] A teetotaller like Florence who was interested in asylum employment (September 1904), must have been very likely to gain employment. The female nurses must not all have been that drawn to drink, for in October 1882 a large number of them applied to have the money equivalent, instead of the beer usually allowed to them.

The problems were no doubt exacerbated by most of the staff actually having to be resident within the asylum walls. Whatever the failings were with any member of staff, to be fair, any recorded examples of staff misdemeanours within the 1st County Asylum Superintendent's Journals, were few and far between. The strict rules and regulations resulted in a tremendous turn over of staff, and may have lessened the opportunities for the young patients to be in the regular company of a familiar face. Once international wars broke out, the situation worsened considerably as when men were called up, they had to go.

Staff were not just required to form strong relationships with each other as part of an effective team, they were also expected to develop relationships with the patients too. The majority of the young patients were admitted at too young an age for them to have loosened any relational bonds with their parents: The asylum staff effectively had to take up the role of their parents. The staff did not always need the Commissioners for Lunacy's rules and regulations for guidance; natural inborn parenting skills would usually adequately suffice.

Maintaining contact with their parents or 'friends' throughout treatment was for some an essential and very strategic part of any positively focused treatment programmes. . For a very small percentage of the young ones, it would be one of the most important routes to recovery. Realistic expectations that they would eventually get back to the home they longed for, was a very strategic part of any cure.

Some youngsters would continue to have access with their parents through actual visits. The 2nd County Asylum had completely separate visiting rooms for males and females to be visited. Records of family members visiting their family members are rarely entered in the case book records as the recording of any visits to patients, did not appear to be a priority in the recording system. The visits from relatives were usually made once a fortnight. Some parts of Leicestershire were over thirty miles from the asylum; this distance could have posed real practical problems for those wishing to visit confined children or teenagers. The foundling Emily[1] was obviously going to be totally deprived of any parental contact. During quick scanning of records there were three children noted to have been specifically visited by a parent: –

Harriett's blind father came to visit her and he must have had some degree of physical contact with his daughter, as he commented that 'she had grown considerably.'

Ida Elizabeth Mary was very pleased to see her father when he called to see her one Saturday.

Thomas[4] 'His friends have been to communicate with him'. January 1882

It was thought questionable how much George Henry (recorded below) would benefit from family visits:–

'Is devoid of affection for his parents or any one else, plays in a silly fashion and makes no request to go home'.

A few would sadly have had minimum if any contact. Family members were invited to annual Christmas celebrations or other significant celebrations such as at the time of specific royal anniversaries – e.g. Queen Victoria's Jubilee Day June 22nd 1897. August 3rd 1896 was a bank holiday and 270 visitors arrived to visit patients in the morning.

For many, liaisons with the other side of the walls involved pen ink and paper. Several of the more literate young patients were encouraged to write to their immediate relatives, so as to maintain reasonable contact. As well as outgoing post, there was the mail in too.

A few of the younger patients were able to visit home. Some of these excursions appear to have been requested by devoted parents who wanted to maintain reasonable levels of contact with their son or daughter.

John William [3] *(Admitted as a 5 year old idiot) 1878 June 6th His parents have taken him home for a week or two - 'Returned well and safely'. 1878 Jun 20th*

Fred was allowed home occasionally for a day or two. Unfortunately, not all the trips home were successful events. Elizabeth [1] in 1884 'She has during the early part of the month been home for a week, but she began to swear and threatened her family.' William [2] went out on a weeks leave, but proved to be unmanageable at home.

A few may have returned home again more permanently, after they had been considered well enough to do so and stayed there: Some though like Naomi Millicent, Muriel and Joseph Montague were discharged 'not improved'. Walter James was also released in the same condition with his 'friends' promising to look after him.

For a few the periods back home were intended as a test, to assess whether they as a patient were ready to be discharged – For Mary [3] admitted with sub–acute mania, it appeared to have been just day trips home with a nurse in attendance. On one of the early visits Mary [3] 'got into a great passion and frightened her mother and sister very much.' After successfully being home twice for an afternoon she was eventually discharged recovered. Edmund's trial sessions back home followed a similar pattern to those of Mary [3]. On his first time out, he was returned to the Asylum by his father, due to him being unmanageable, but after a few more attempts, he was discharged recovered too.

Families were contacted when there were worrying changes in their sons or daughters health:–

Arthur [4] 1886 June 13th 'Having somewhat severe fits, and is very feeble – his mother written to about him'.

William [3] 1880 Nov 13th 'Father has been written to – Quite a temperature Cold cloths to head'.

Willie 1890 Oct 14th Wrote to father – 16th October 1890 Died 5.40 am Tubercular phthisis Nurse E Morgan

Tragically, for many it appears from the records, that the contact for many was essentially just mainly in one direction – from asylum to home. It was essential therefore that the other adults, the asylum staff, would be empathic enough in their profession, for the days, weeks, months and years within the walls to have been experienced whenever possible relatively happily as a form of 'home from home'.

Basics of Asylum Care

The Reception Orders for admission had been verified: The Medical Officers on initial entry had completed their examinations, assessments and the first paper work: Those of 'such tender years' had become asylum patients in what would be for them immense pieces of architecture.

> 'There they stand, isolated, majestic, imperious, brooded over by the gigantic water-tower and chimney combined, rising unmistakable and daunting out of the countryside – the asylum which our forefathers built with such immense solidity'. Enoch Powell, Minister of Health 1961[26]

Caring for many hundreds of patients required incredible and flexible organisational skills. The buildings were continually being extended or modified, at one time the 1st County Asylum had to construct wooden buildings to house the ever increasing numbers of patients and they were nicknamed 'the huts'. In June 1872 the shed in the Engineer's Yard at the Borough Asylum had to be converted into a temporary hospital for smallpox cases.[27] The buildings were well maintained with constant records of repairs or redecoration of various sections. Certain modernisations were also happening.

Ward image 1

Ward image 2

The much younger patients must have been housed mostly alongside hundreds of adult patients. Males and females of any age were in completely separate wards or blocks. The male and female wards were usually in completely separate areas. Details are not included as to which wards the young ones were admitted to with the exception of the fragile infant males who would often be located in a female ward. At Berrywood Asylum

26   Leicestershire's Lunatics – The Institutional care of Leicester shire's Lunatics during the Nineteenth Century H G Orme W H Brock Leicestershire Museums and Art Galleries 1987 ISBN 085022 227 3

27   Borough Superintendents Journal DE2853–40

in Northamptonshire there had been a specific new block created in 1887 for 'idiot' and 'imbecile' children adjacent to the female wing. One of the 4 year olds named Cecil from Market Harborough was only a County patient for a month and was probably relocated to Berrywood, Asylum so that he was able to be with other children. On the preceding page are photographs of two wards from the 1st County Asylum, which do not appear to show the sleeping facilities[28] –

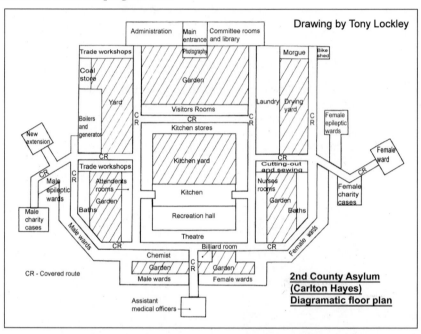

Drawing by Tony Lockley

2nd County Asylum
(Carlton Hayes)
Diagramatic floor plan

The above architect's original plan (not to scale) of the 2nd County Asylum shows the general layout of the wards. The ward blocks were entitled epileptic, "sick and infirm", "recent" and "acute" and "charity" cases. The numbers of patients in these wards ranged from one in 76 single wards, with all the other beds being in dormitories with 12, 24, 26, or 48 beds. The image opposite shows a 48–bed dormitory, which was specifically for epileptics[29].

28   Stewart Collection Photograph courtesy of Leicestershire, Leicester and Rutland Record Office.
29   Photograph courtesy of the Record Office for Leicestershire, Leicester & Rutland. DE3533/380B

Many of these juvenile admissions were young by both actual age and mental age. For the asylum to function efficiently as their new residence, it would firstly have to empathically cater for their very basic 'home from home' needs. They would need to be fed, clothed, rested, kept warm and kept both clean and dry. There would also of course be a need for them to be warmly approached by both the adult staff and patients.

One of the very first avenues of care in the asylum was to ensure that the very basic dietary needs were met. For some regular and substantial meals would have been very far from their usual fare back at home. Certain incoming patients had previously experienced horrendous privations in food, due to poverty stricken households. One tragic example of just how bad it was for some comes in the casebook records of four–year–old Arthur [4] from Hugglescote. He had apparently, prior to admission been accustomed to live solely on bread alone and after a more nutritious diet at the asylum, including beef tea:–

> *'He soon gained colour to his previous milk white cheeks and firmness to his flesh'.*

The only direct improvement treatment brought for the multiply impaired Frederick [3] in February 1871, was through his daily diet: –

> *'Has gained flesh slightly since his admission, otherwise there is nothing to be noted in this case'.*

Not everyone at the time of admission had a healthy appetite and there were a couple of young patients whose appetites were poor, or they exhibited a 'disinclination to food' and just would not eat. They were obviously successfully encouraged to partake of food, as no under fourteen year olds appear to have been fed by means of a stomach pump or via an oesophageal tube, as some adults were.

Quite a few of the incoming fourteen and under, were unable to do anything for themselves, which included being fairly dependent at meal times. Mabel Kezziah, Charles [1], Olive, Lily and Cecil were all recorded this way.

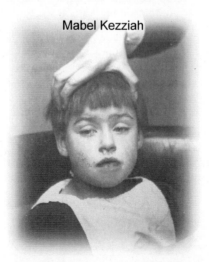

Mabel Kezziah

A few could handle a spoon to feed themselves, but many did it in a rather clumsy manner. Some would eat with their fingers if they were not carefully assisted at meal times. Gertrude had to be fed, as otherwise she would cram food into her mouth too rapidly. The information of any dietary trends throughout the records, are mainly of what they should not have been devouring, which included their own faeces, or anything else that was not appropriate for digestion. Several of those with learning difficulties had problems with their salivary glands and would be constantly dribbling. John Alpheus had this complication, together with him at times also regurgitating food.

Under the superintendent's leadership, there was an incredible amount of pre–planning that went into one of the most significant times of the asylum day, he ensured that both patients and staff had meals that were worth coming to the table for. The quality of the food that arrived on the dining tables was of paramount importance to the asylum superintendents and there are constant, regular entries in their journals related to it. The Superintendent recorded any dissatisfaction with any part of the diet regardless of whether it was from patients or staff in his journals. Admirably, the following phrase was a regular inclusion:–

'The provisions have been of good quality and well cooked'.[30]

Preparing a nutritious diet for hundreds of patients and staff must have been a monumental task. The 2nd County Asylum's food kitchen comprised of the cook's office, a scullery, large ovens (needing a coal store), a crockery store, a bake house with a cooling room, a fresh meat store, a vegetable store, a vegetable preparation room, a dairy and two larders.

All this activity in the kitchen lead to meal times, which for many of the young ones must have been the very best time of the day. Naomi Millicent always began to cry about half an hour before meals. Some had severely deficient communication skills, but eight–year–old Edgar William understood enough to go to the dining area when he was called at meal times. Henry [3] would show evident signs of pleasure when his food was taken to him. William [5] had a voracious appetite and would make grunting noises before the meal times. Elizabeth[2] obviously enjoyed her food as she took it ravenously.

Various officials from the outside kept any of the Superintendent's decisions under their watchful eye, coming to check on many things, and one of those items was the food. They not only looked, they tasted it:–

'Dinner which was much improved and which all appeared to enjoy. Dinner consisted of soup, Bread and Plumb pudding'.[31]

Only a few recordings were found of any specially prepared diets. There was Arthur[4] with his beef tea. For the last few months of his life, Henry's [3] diet was chiefly 'a little mild swill'. In 1856 Maria [2] was kept in bed and ordered 'No 1 diet' but no records were found of what this may have consisted of. Mary Jane at one time was 'placed on a

30   Borough Superintendents Journal 1 DE2853–40
31   Asylum House Visitors Book 20th January 1893 DE3533–9A

nutritious, carefully regulated diet. The current 'five a day' would have struggled within the asylum's 19 Century diet as a liberal and nutritious diet, was apparently a diet 'without any vegetables'.[32] As well as the journal entries, there were diet sheets that were displayed in the main hall of the 1st County Asylum, for the public and other visitors to see. The components of the asylum diets were continually under close scrutiny.

Leading members of staff kept themselves aware of anything new and in September 1876, Dr Rothsay Stewart from the County Asylum had announced –

'I desire to draw your attention to some new preparations of tinned meat - Compressed corned beef from Chicago. Taking it will be useful as an article of diet for use in this asylum'. 13th Sept 1876 ...

In 1906 New Zealand mutton was brought in as the American tinned meat was discontinued. The new innovative technologies did not necessarily effect an appreciated influence on the diet:–

'Meat in cold storage slightly unpleasant taste'. 28th Oct 1907 [33]

If the quality of any dietary component was doubted, the experts were called in. Just one example of this, was in 1875 when the cheese was thought to be not up to standard. An experienced cheese buyer therefore arrived to taste it and he felt that it was not good enough. If necessary, in later years, samples would be made of certain foodstuffs, such as from the 'Libbys' tinned meat in July 1907, which was taken for analysis.

Bread was a very essential part of the diet and its quality was always under watchful eyes and taste buds. The bread that arrived on the asylum's dining tables throughout several centuries was bound to vary. Both the County and Borough Asylum Superintendent's Journals noted various ups and downs with their daily loaves. Bread arriving from local bakers in July 1857 was either described as being of 'very objectionable character' or 'uniformly good'. The difficulty in getting good quality bread was probably one of the reasons why the County Asylum eventually built a baker's shop in 1883 and made their own loaves. Problems were not over with the quality of bread, even when they baked their own, for eventually the major component of bread, the flour contracted in to bake the bread, was at times of inferior quality. The thickness of the slice was altered in August 1891: –

'Thinner slices of bread reduced from 6 and 5 ounce pieces to 4 ounces'.

In the 1900's, breadbaskets were placed on the tables during dinner times (for the 1st County Asylum) so that patients were able to help themselves to what they required. In 1889 the patients could not apparently tell 'Stork from butter', as when margarine was on several occasions substituted for butter, the change was not noted and no complaints were made.

32 County Asylum Case Book DE3533–185–736
33 Journal VI Borough Superintendents Journal DE2853–45

The milk was also high on the list for ensuring its quality was maintained. The superintendents of both asylums made considerable efforts, to ensure good quality milk was given to the patients. The milk either came from the Asylum Farms, or was brought in by a private contractor. The Borough Asylum had far more problems with the milk that was brought in, than the 1st County Asylum. In 1886 the Borough's milk was recorded as being collected from the station. In May 1882 the County Asylum's milk was noted as being very good and much appreciated by the patients. It is recorded 'as containing 10 per cent of cream, according to the use of a graduated glass'[34]. The worst incident within the Borough Asylum milk was in 1878, when it was found to be so bad that a specialist at the asylum made an analysis. A Mr Harris discovered that the milk was adulterated with 33 per cent of water. [35] Due to the poor quality of milk deliveries in 1895 one of the superintendents went out to Thurnby Lodge farm from where future replacement deliveries were due to come from:–

> *'The water for washing the milk utensils is obtained from a newly made well the situation of which is satisfactory as far as regards the drainage from the farm yard. Mr Wright the farmer says the water has been analysed and found to be quite free from impurity. There are four young children who appear to be in robust health. I also inspected the cow sheds and other out buildings and I have come to the conclusion that it will be safe to allow Mr Wright to supply the asylum with milk'. Friday 17th May 1895*[36]

Milk was of course not the only fluid to pass the patients lips. Alcohol was usually part of the diet and for some adult patients it was actually a part of the treatment. Tea was a more common drink and in October 1891, the official visitors tasted it on one of their regular visits and it was found to be 'quite equal to sample'. [37] Chocolate was perhaps for many quite a stranger to their taste buds, as in June 1905 a large number of patients objected to having cocoa for breakfast twice a week.[38] In March 1908 it was suggested 'that a trial should be given to Bovril for the preparation of beef tea for the sick.' The patients were also noted as having glasses of lemonade specially concocted for the regular dances. One wonders what drinks the young ones would have had direct access to.

Several inclusions are made within the Borough Journals of certain occasional treats. A local speciality 'rabbit pie' arrived on the menu several times and it was always very much appreciated. The rabbit pie was a much enjoyed occasion, all of its own, but there were other specific times of the year when certain delicacies arrived at the asylum tables. Christmas dinner always seemed to to have included plum puddings for the desserts. On Shrove Tuesday 'the patients had the usual pancake puddings' (19th February 1901). On Good Friday 'Hot Cross Buns for tea were of excellent quality' (5th April 1901). On Easter Day (7th April 1901) roast veal and bacon was recorded as the usual dinner for Easter lunch. On Coronation Day (22nd June 1911) the staff and patients were treated to extra fare and a dance in the evening. A Special Account Cash Book[39] from the Borough

---

34   County Superintendents Journal DE3533–85
35   Journal 2 Borough Superintendent's Journal DE2853–41
36   Borough Superintendent's Diary DE2853–65
37   Asylum House Visitors Book DE3533–9A
38   Borough Superintendent's Journal DE2853–45 – VI
39   Special Account Cash Book Borough Asylum DE2853–33

Asylum also shows other certain treats such as buns (June 1877), aerated waters (1881 and 1905), lemon syrup (July 1884), lime juice (August 1895), ginger ale (June 1877), cowslip wine (July 1881) plus sweets (June 1883) reclassified as confectionary in September 1908.

Another major part of the asylum day, was the hours spent asleep, at night time. An essential part of recovery or noticeable relief was a good night's sleep. Helping to ensure patients of any age got a reasonable night's slumber was a major part of the treatment. One of the behaviours clearly defined on admission, was on how well the incoming patient slept:–

> *'His appetite is good and he sleeps well'. John* [2]

> *'Sleeps quietly takes his food well'. Edmund.*

> *'Is clean in her habits and sleeps fairly well'. Janet Winnie*

The medical officer on admission must have been relieved to record such satisfactory habits, for his new young patients, as this was sadly, often, very very far from the case. Walter was not only sleepless at night he was quite noisy too. It was questionable whether 'sleeps well' would still be able to happen, in what was quite frequently an exceptionally noisy asylum environment. Violet Anne and her restless nights and maladjusted behaviours were quite empathically approached within her case book records:–

> *'If annoyed she lies down on the floor and screams and it is only occasionally that her confidence can be gained'.*

Violet Anne

The adults were noisy: The young ones could join them and be noisy too. Mary [3] following admission with sub–acute mania was understandably quite unsettled and would sing through most of the night and part of the following day as well. Elizabeth [1] made a great noise at night as she said that 'she could hear her mother calling her' in October 1867. Thirteen–year–old Alfred [1] had been quite unmanageable at home, shouting and squealing at night, disturbing all the neighbours. On admission he initially continued this behaviour and kept other patients in his dormitory awake. Young Elizabeth [2] was also very noisy at night, screaming and making loud incoherent cries. There was John William [1], a deaf and dumb imbecile. He would tend not to sleep at night and keeping everyone in his bedroom awake, with the noise that he made, but was himself unable to hear! Several other youngsters were noted for being sleepless and noisy at night without causing major long–term disruption. One of the noisiest must have been Naomi Millicent:–

> *'Throws herself about in bed. Dec 8th 1902 Has frequent bouts of crying for no apparent reason - disturbs the whole neighbourhood - so that it is very trying to be near her on such occasions - is the most noisy patient in the institution...As noisy as ever - howls for hours at a time.... Requires sedative draughts frequently.... In a single room as she was very noisy- yells for hours at the top of her voice'.*

Sarah Susan Ravina was also so constantly noisy at night screaming and yelling that she also required a side room. . (In the 2nd County Asylum Records, in a plan of the lay out of all the buildings, states there were 79 single rooms)[40]. Elizabeth [3] caused similar problems and made the most piteous sound, a cross between a cry and a roar of anger. She was quite dry eyed and none of the staff could find a reason for her doing so. She would keep it up for hours and when she started, kept everybody in her ward awake at night, unless she was also quietened with a sedative.

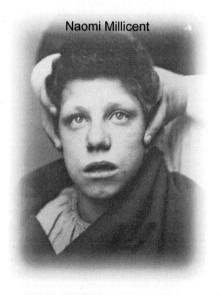

Naomi Millicent

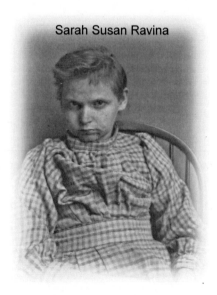

Sarah Susan Ravina

---

40   Lay out of Asylum Buildings DE3421–10 (See Page 66)

Those who suffered from epilepsy often had their sleep patterns disrupted by convulsions at night. Young Walter rarely passed a night without a fit. Jonathan suffering from epileptic mania had epileptic fits almost every night, coupled with frequent ones in the day too. Fred would have epileptic fits both day and night. A William [9] who had been afflicted with epilepsy for four years, would suffer from sleeplessness for a night or two after having had a fit. The most severe epileptics would require to be placed in a special ward together, with the keenly suicidal, so that they would have a special night watch from staff. Maria Martha had to be eventually specifically placed in one of the epileptic dormitories, due to the severity of her convulsions. One member of staff was required to sleep in or near every dormitory and each dormitory was either to have a light burning all night, or a means of immediately obtaining one.

The asylums had their padded rooms, which offered safety to the excessively maniacal patients. These rooms are rarely mentioned in the case books, a juvenile patient being placed in one in 1845:–

> *'..during the intervals between the fits she is active and lively - but somewhat noisy, but when under the influence of them she is a perfect fiend destroying everything that she can lay her hands upon and inflicting violence to herself and her attendants during these times. She requires personal restraint not only on her own account but also on that of those whose duty it is to attend to her. The diet has been carefully regulated and she sleeps in a padded room'. Elizabeth Mary*

This appears to be the only mention of a 'padded room' for those aged fourteen and under on admission, most of the young ones slept in a completely unrestrained setting. For Emily [2] an 'idiot' admitted in March 1847 her bed became her free space:–

> *'...and instead of always being fastened in a chair, which has hitherto been done by her Friends, to be allowed to roll about on a bed upon the floor - nothing but education will avail in this case'.*

A couple of those with learning difficulties did not sleep on a bed, which was raised above the ground. Patients like John [1] were in consequence of their epilepsy, much safer sleeping on the floor. Young Millicent was described as 'a strange creature' in 1880. She was quite 'violent and impulsive at times – destructive to articles of crockery and clothes'. She would only sleep at night on the ground with a ticking rug. Four years on from her original admission date, she still had her comforter – her 'ticking rug' with her on the asylum floor.

Another essential part of effective treatment and care was to keep the youngsters warm. Fortunately, the purchase of American stoves at the 1st County Asylum in 1874 lessened the danger of access to so many open fires, but the hot doors were still a danger to many. Even when central heating (July 1902) arrived at the turn of the century there was note of

> *'No further steps have been taken to protect the patients from being injured by the radiators in the wards and dormitories'. July 1902[41]*

---

41 Journal V Superintendents Journal DE3533–88

As well as being kept warm the patients needed to be kept clean. Achieving this undertaking involved an incredible amount of hard work and a constant supply of water. With the 1ˢᵗ County Asylum, the local waterworks company was unfortunately at times exceptionally unreliable in either providing enough of it, or in providing water of a reasonable quality. The supply was noted several times as being of a very interrupted character and the Superintendent had to make arrangements for the asylum's own well to be used. In December 1893 the official visitors had seen the analysis of the water from the Asylum's own well and regretted that it was entirely unfit for drinking purposes.[42]

Water for bathing purposes was required to be hot. The Asylum Superintendent seemed at times to be having more problems with the asylum heating requirements than the patients themselves. There were frequent journal entries relating to innumerable problems with boilers and pumps, chimneys, engines and pipes. If it was not a problem with boiler then it was difficulties with the actual coal supplies to run it:–

> *'In view of the imminent coal strike and of others that may succeed in the future, it is respectfully suggested that as soon as may be conveniently carried out, a stock of coal be laid up on the Asylum grounds say 100 tons, so as to obviate the terrible straits the Institution would be thrown into in case at any time should the contractor be unable to draw the daily supply. We live now as regards the supply of coal from hand to mouth and often have less than a ton in the Coal Yard'. 9ᵗʰ March 1892"[43]*

Developing the patients own independence skills eased the situation but it was a task for both staff and young patients. There were very strict rules for bath procedures and specific bath timetables, any member of staff not following the rules received strict reprimands, sometimes losing a days leave. Not all of the young ones including William[8] enjoyed the bathing procedures:–

> *'When bathed he sometimes screams and struggles as if he was being murdered'.*

Eventually, it was not just baths, as new body cleansing technology arrived at the Borough Asylum:–

> *'The spray baths have been used experimentally and are found to give great satisfaction, they are much liked by the patients'. 1914 5ᵗʰ May*

As well as being clean they had to be dry. With so many who were completely incontinent on admission, it would be at times a formidable task to keep them clean and dry. Those suffering from continual incontinence must have been kept incredibly clean, as only one mention of skin problems, or any form of 'nappy rash', (due to poor toileting habits), was found in the records–

> *'He often gets excoriation of the abdomen from his so often wetting himself'. Henry* [3]

42   Journal IV Superintendents Journal DE3533–88
43   Journal IV Superintendents Journal DE3533–88

Just how clean and dry they must have been kept is evidenced by the quantities of washing that the asylum laundries were handling. In one week in December 1862, the number of pieces of laundry washed in the County Asylum was totalled and subsequently recorded in the Superintendent's Journal – the figures are astounding: –

> *The increasing quantity of linen used in the asylum (now amounting to 4015 pieces per week) is more than the servants and patients can properly manage'.*[44]

The toileting abilities of the youngsters being admitted, like young Joseph from Oakthorpe, must have certainly markedly contributed to the stacks of washing being laundered in the 1ˢᵗ asylum's laundry. Nearly half of those aged fourteen and under were incontinent at the time of admission.

Clean	23	16%
Not known	34	24%
Probably incontinent	19	15%
Incontinent	61	45%

The pressure these statistics must have placed on staff in the wards and in the laundry must have been considerable. The incontinence levels with some of their co–patients, before the era of more modern fabrics, plastic sheeting and disposable sanitary materials must have caused phenomenal stacks of laundry.[45]

There were several inclusions in the Superintendent's Journals for the Borough Asylum regarding the laundry facilities. In 1911 Oct 2ⁿᵈ there is the following entry about a section that probably had to deal with the washing for those who were incontinent – Including the young and never successfully toilet trained, but also the senile and the desperately ill:–

> *The range of slate soaking troughs in the wash-house requires to be replaced as most of them are too dilapidated to be repaired. - A small soap boiling copper is desirable for the foul wash-house'.*[46]

This pre–cleansed washing would probably have eventually ended up in grand scale washing machines. In December 1894, the Bradford Washing Machine (at the Borough) was found to be inadequate to properly wash the large increase in quantity of clothes. In 1904 the same machine parts, the castings, after 25 years of service, were recorded as being very worse for wear. Later in 1904 there is note of repairs being required to a Manlove Washing machine. At one point a Borough Committee member had heard about the Hill and Company of Leicester's new Washing Machine, but he had to go all the way down to a public laundry in Harrow Road in London, to actually watch one

---

44   Superintendent's Journal County Asylum DE3533–84
45   Sunneyholme Account Records– A home for feeble minded girls in 1924 where twelve yards of rubber sheeting is being purchased. It is not clear when this type of sheeting was first available for use in Leicestershire Asylums. DE3107–197
46   Superintendent's Journal Borough Asylum DE2853–45 Journal VI

at work.[47] The laundry staff and patients would also be using the wringing machines which in May 1895 were in the same operational difficulties as the washing machines had been.

There were so many processes for some of the laundry to go through. Soaking troughs, boiling coppers, washing machines, mangling, wringing, drying in the drying closets on the drying horses or drying slides. Male patients were recorded as sometimes helping with the mangles. At the 2nd County Asylum there is an enormous drying yard on the architect's plan. A flannel drying area is specified on the same plan and this could be linked to sanitary protection for those who were incontinent. After the drying came the ironing on the 'ironing stones' or calendering (which involved the use of ironing machines with rollers using a combination of moisture, heat and pressure). Both these systems had safety guards in place.

The incontinent young ones were also likely to have been more appropriately clothed within the asylum, than they previously were at home, due to the extensive laundry facilities that were then available, a busy tailor's shop actually on site and female patients very adept with needles and pins. The task of keeping the youngsters reasonably clothed must have been provoked by a number of children who were all renowned clothes rippers.

A few of those with mental illness, took up just as much staff time, when it came to dressing themselves as those with severe learning difficulty. Thomas [7] with mania would not dress himself. William [6] was continually taking his coat and waistcoat off. Some were in fact quite resistant to being dressed or undressed. Agnes hated being undressed for bed in the evenings. Whereas the young Mary Elizabeth: –

> *'Does not seem to care whether she is dressed or not as long as she is allowed to play'.*

Some times understandable adjustments were made to what was actually worn. Horace was promoted to knickerbockers a week after his admission, another lad Henry[3] was, a month after his admission in May 1865, also given other articles of clothing:–

> *'Provided with trousers instead of the petticoats in which he was brought to the asylum and his habits of playing with his genitals have been materially checked by these means'.*

Appropriate clothing ensured that the young patients would be kept warm. It was also essential that the same patients should experience a degree of inner warmth provided by the company they kept. The asylum staff and some of the adult patients effectively provided the very basics of care, often with a little bit extra too. With so many adults around to participate in this care, it could perhaps have been experienced at a higher and more efficient level, than could ever have been managed at home.

---

47 Superintendent's Diary Borough Asylum DE2853–66

Medical Treatment

The lunatic asylums were later to become mental hospitals. Whatever else was happening to the new admissions within the asylums, they were essentially being nursed and cared for as hospital patients. Their general health was treated and not just their mental health, with their physical health being at times easier to treat. Millicent's physical health quite quickly improved but she was still occasionally hysterical and violent in her conduct. Elizabeth [3] was quite critically ill on admission and in consequence must have received high levels of nursing.

It was the nurses, the attendants and other adults who made sure that the very basic needs were met: It was the doctors, the medical men, who were there to diagnose conditions and to administer various treatments. Part of any potential cure or relief from certain conditions, would be the prescription of certain medicines. Maria [2] on her second admission for chronic mania had her medical situation noted in 1853 as follows.

'She is occasionally intractable for a few hours and has had no occasion for medical treatment - Beyond a little house medicine occasionally'.

Jonathan who had become increasingly feeble and William [2] who was losing flesh were both put on 'tonics'. Several, who were probably suffering from some form of anaemia, were prescribed a form of iron with Mary [3] having a grain of sulphate of iron. James [3] was tragically described as a:–

'Wretched anaemic spectacle'.

Other prescriptive compounds such as quinine were recorded. On admission Elizabeth [1] was found to have severely costive bowels, so she was therefore immediately prescribed some purgative medicine. Mary Jane with epileptic mania was ordered some 'cooling aperient' medicine. Alcohol was also used as a prescriptive tool to aid recovery and even the younger ones, eventually as grown ups within the asylum received it too, John Alpheus was being given port wine in 1882 at the age of 18.

The young admissions must have been very much aware of others receiving medication as William [8] in 1896 was asking almost every morning for some 'black draught' for his toothache. Thomas [8] an imbecile from Lutterworth would often try to find an ailment as an excuse for taking medicine, but Agnes would only take her medicine if it were masked in her food. The 1st County Asylum had a specific Prescription Book (which unfortunately has not survived), but the continual mention of it, within a high percentage of the case books pages– 'vide prescription book' is clear evidence of how continually, prescriptively treated the young ones were.

Medications were frequently prescribed to try to relieve the epileptic condition.. Both Arthur [4] and Sarah Jane in 1895 took Borax and bromide with 'excellent results'.

'Borax Gr 7 ½ Pot Brom gr 15 twice a day with good effect'. Sarah Jane 1895 Aug 20th

Bromide was such a common prescription for epilepsy, that William [9] in 1907 had developed the side effect of a 'bromide rash'. Others were prescribed 'chloral drafts' as part of their potential cure. One patient who was admitted as a 15 year old epileptic 'imbecile', suffered a series of severe epileptic seizures and was put to bed, but when his fits did not cease:–

> *'He was given a soap and water enema this did not diminish the severity of the seizures eventually the patient had two very strong ones and died at 5-17 pm in the presence of J Hill Attendant'. - Cause Of Death - Exhaustion from epilepsy.*[48]

There were various degrees of intensity of epilepsy to be treated – 'How Strong' – 'How Often' and' How Long'. Walter James and Jonathan had epileptic episodes at night. For some like Mabel it was just 'slight sensations' Both John William [3] and Mabel were fortunate in just experiencing the less intensive 'petit mal' form of the disease. The frequency of the fits was potentially just as draining as their actual intensity. Eunice was fortunate in just having 3 or 4 epileptic episodes a year. Some had such a severe succession of fits that they went into 'status'. For Maria Martha they were 'infrequent': For Muriel it was a fit or fits every day. Some had 'an uninterrupted succession of fits'. Almost a dozen patients had the term 'frequent' used. The lucky ones were those that had long or a virtually permanent period of remission: With Ida Winifred for example being recorded as having her first fit in seven years. The unlucky ones were those that ended up having an exhausting life threatening succession of fits:–

> *'Last night she had 67 epileptic fits in succession'. Mary Ann* [2]. *26th Sept 1886*

The fits were meticulously recorded. There must have been other paper work where the single epileptic episodes would have been recorded. For William [9] his number of fits were recorded for quarters[49]:–

> *'Suffers from sleeplessness for a night or two after having a fit. Has suffered from epilepsy for four years.*
>
> 1908 Jan 10 Is troublesome and broke a window Had 42 fits last quarter
>
> 1908 April 10 Is very troublesome and destructive. 68 fits last quarter
>
> 1908 July 10th Is still very troublesome 75 fits last quarter'

The following entries of his epileptic fits, two years later, are even more astounding:–

> April 23rd Day 56 night 70
>
> April 24th Day 146 night 130
>
> April 25th Day 84 night 63
>
> April 26th Day 10 night 43
>
> April 27th Day 20 night 40
>
> April 28th Day 200 night none since 5 o'clock

---

48   William Arthur admitted at the age of 15. DE2853–195–5452
49   Case Book Extract Copy Courtesy of Leicestershire, Leicester and Rutland Record Office DE3533–206 Page 90

William's [9] epileptic experiences were horrendous but the individual's experience of epilepsy could vary. Some who had always had night–time fits, others would have them in the day too. Rapid regular small fits, could become rarely occurring, intense convulsions. The epileptic episodes had various effects on the young patients. Some became 'comatose', Harriet was semiconscious and Violet Anne would be partially conscious for several days, Sarah Elizabeth was 'more lost than she usually was, and 'at times hardly understands what she is doing'. Many others would be left in a heavy stupor or a severely exhausted state, One lad named William [6] was much luckier, as he eventually improved, no longer always falling down, and instead 'just being lost for a minute or two and standing quite still whilst he recovered himself.'

Any type of visible bodily change or damage was almost always recorded within the casebook records. The epilepsy sufferers had more than their fair share of cuts and bruises plus more severe incidents of wounds to their bodies. Thomas [3] who went in his epileptic and idiotic state regularly out to the farm, was recorded in April 1898 to have fallen due to a fit and on two occasions he had actually buried his face in falling. Severe epileptic events happening during the night, could often inadvertently lead to death, if they were not immediately observed:–

'Henry [2] was found by attendant Smith this morning about half past 3 o'clock dead. He had been dead only a short time as was ascertained by writer H Thornley who were both called to the deceased - he was found lying upon his face and had evidently died from epileptic convulsions of which he had many during the preceding few days'. 1ˢᵗ October 1875

One of the most tragic injuries resulting in accidental death must have been the case of a 7 year old 'idiot' named John William [3]: –

'I regret I have to report a deplorable accident which occurred to a patient an epileptic and idiotic child on the 25th May. This patient John William aged 7 was admitted about 2 years ago from Thorpe Satchville and on the day mentioned fell while in a fit, into the fire place of his ward by which means his clothes caught fire and he received considerable but superficial burns thereby, and he died on the following day of shock to the nervous system'.⁵⁰ 9th June 1880 Cause of death 'ambustio'

The least likely to have an accident, due to epilepsy, were those who gave fair warning that an epileptic episode was imminent – John [2] would yell quite loudly for ½ a minute prior to a fit. Harriett became more excitable often rushing around the airing court. Arthur [2] would have a 'wry face like a child commencing to cry. The following phrases were a regular inclusion within many patient case records:–

'With the exception of his epilepsy he/she is in good health'.

Not everyone was that lucky. The convulsions would for example understandably influence a patient's appetite – 'has taken no appreciable amount of food for some days.' William [4] had to be moved from his ward, in consequence of him falling so often out of his bed during the night in fits.

---

50   1st County Superintendent's Journal DE3533–86

A patient's general behaviour pattern could also understandably be extremely negatively affected by epilepsy. For some their epilepsy had caused defective intellect. The maniacal excitement William [7] experienced was complicated by epilepsy. Many as a consequence of epilepsy had quite variable temporary derangements. Some became exceptionally violent, troublesome and destructive often due to the epilepsy itself causing a great deal of excitement. Several were noted as being dirty in their habits following fits (non–empathic words for those who had involuntary lack of control of bladders and bowels during epilepsy). Others would suffer injury and furniture and windows would be broken. One of the recorders appeared to have some empathy for those with the convulsive condition: –

> *'In the interval after recovering from an epileptic attacks he has fits of most uncontrollable temper in which I do not consider he is responsible for his actions'.*

The cause of death or the death certificate is not always part of the case book records, but for those where the specific reason is included almost twenty died from epileptic convulsions.

The youngsters once admitted did not only have learning difficulty or mental illness, often coupled with epilepsy, they had other illnesses and infections, which had of course to be treated too. The health of Donald rapidly deteriorated when he lost power in his lower extremities. Meticulous records were made when they were otherwise ill, with temperature charts often being part of a patient's notes.

In any era, infectious diseases have caused problems and it was no different in an asylum in Leicestershire in the 19th and early 20th Century. The priority was always to stop the infections outside the walls coming in. A strategic ploy to keep infections out was to have some degree of control over those who came in. This was not always easy when patients with well–established infectious diseases had their certificate of admission.

> *'Charles ... was admitted today from the Leicester Union. He is recovering from an attack of smallpox but a medical certificate was sent, stating that there was no fear of contagion. I have however had him placed in the temporary hospital'.*[51] *24th July 1872*

> *'A female patient from Union was refused admission because she was suffering from erysipelas'. March 5th 1875*

The Asylum Officers efficiently kept themselves up to date with any infectious diseases on the outside. In 1882 the Police went to the Borough Asylum to report a case of smallpox in Humberstone. [52]. Even fish orders from Grimsby were stopped due to cholera being rife in the town in September 1893. An asylum carter was suspended from duty and sent home in November 1892 due to one of his children having contracted

---

51 Borough Superintendent's Journal 1 DE2853–40
52 Borough Superintendent's Journal 1 DE2853–40

scarlet fever.[53] During epidemics – smallpox in 1854, 1872 and 1877, scarlet fever in 1882, 1893 and 1896 and diphtheria in 1900, more stringent visiting rules came into force (sometimes visits were completely suspended) and fewer patients were allowed out on parole. On Christmas Eve 1896 'great precautions were taken from any one coming to the special seasonal entertainment, from any house infected with Scarlet Fever'.

It was of course imperative that infection levels were kept down within the asylums themselves. Eventually, considerations for purchasing any new technologies, such as the 'Thresh's Formation Disinfector 'at a probable cost of £35',[54] may have helped to play a major role in keeping the germs at bay. The New Zealand and Australian Armed Forces also had one the same machines for each division as part of the Gallipoli Campaign. Hospitals for infectious diseases were opened in the town and county and special arrangements were also made to convert certain asylum rooms to become special wards when infectious diseases were rife. When Janet Winnie caught Scarlet Fever in October 1909, she had to be removed to an Isolation Hospital. Various other epidemics struck the asylums. Sarah contracted an illness in the county asylum in 1864, which was firstly named 'dysentery', but the cause of her death from this infection was recorded as 'typhoid'

More serious epidemics within the asylum caused phenomenal problems when the staff were infected too. In 1891 the County Asylum was in upheaval due to one of the influenza epidemics:–

> *'Great inconvenience has ensued in carrying on the work, as the diminished staff had not only the sick patients to attend to but their sick fellow-servants as well - on the whole we have managed very well, although all the kitchen servants were ill at one time and the baker succumbed two days ago and had to go home. The cooking has been carried on very well indeed by AM Jno Smith who was 20 years in the Army and used to cook for his mess at times'.[55]*

The younger patients were also affected by the diseases of childhood too. Mary [1] picked up chickenpox in March 1884 and in January 1893 'had a peculiar cough like the "hoop"'. Certain strains may have been kept away from them, due to their isolation from other children, which was enabled by the asylum walls and gates. Four young ones were noted as being really ill with tonsillitis. Poor Emily [1] was so frequently subject to the throat condition that hers were recorded as being permanently enlarged. Little Arthur [4] was in agony at one time with his cracked chilblains.

It was not just certain medicines prescribed for various conditions as in the asylum earlier years leeches were used too. They became so popular as a form of remedy, for various bodily conditions, that eventually shiploads had to be imported from Australia to meet the needs of the British medical men.[56] The little creatures were part of

53   Borough Superintendent's Journal 1 DE2853–40
54   1st County Superintendent's Journals DE3533–90
55   1st County Superintendents Journals DE3533–88
56   Australian Geographic No 14 April–June+ 1989 Leech Mania Graeme Sims

Elizabeth Mary's records in 1845.

> *'She has been leeched and blistened and requires medicine continually to check the constitutional tendency to obesity'.*

Whenever influenza struck it was given written acclamation in the Medical Superintendent's Journals as a worrying problem, which should be recorded, but the attitude towards the high incidence of phthisis, appeared to be that. – It is so much part of life on both sides of the walls and there is nothing we can do about it, given towards it. William [8] in April 1889 had shown signs of commencing phthisis that winter but it was improved through cod liver oil being prescribed.

As patients within an asylum they did though have the constant availability of a doctor and a nurse at any hour of the day or night. The National Health Service was yet to arrive.

Training Programmes

Another essential part of any time spent within the asylum walls by the younger
patients, was them undertaking any training they were able to receive whilst there.
There were no block individual training programmes found within the records: There
were just very informative lines noted within many other lines of information in the case
books.

There were four priorities within any training programmes:–

a) It was imperative that they should be safe during their time spent as a patient.

b) Their social skills should be more enabled to encourage better independence.

c) Every patient should be spending their time as well as could be expected, in view
of their individual capabilities.

d) Those that were not designated as incurable needed to be being prepared for
their potential return to the outside world again.

Safety, was the very first priority as it had been within their dwellings prior to admission.
To maintain safety levels both for themselves and others, patients of all ages were kept
under a very watchful eye. Those who were suicidal or suffering from severe epilepsy
required a double watch and at one time were allocated 'a red ticket' (There is no
further information as to what this involved). At one time the names of these patients
were written on a list, which was pinned on the wall. It was during keen observations
that the appropriateness of a patient's behaviour within the daily asylum routines was
judged. Their daily conduct would of course often govern the activities they were given
access to.

It must not be thought that all of the young patients, exhibited behavioural difficulties,
as this certainly was not the case. A few new admissions needed little if any corrections
of their behaviour and were presumably admitted to receive treatment to 'make better'
rather than to be contained:–

*'She was cleanly in person and appeared very docile and willing to conform to
the regulations of the asylum'. Maria* [2]

*'This little girl is very well behaved and quiet in the ward and a very great
favourite with everybody'. Emily* [1]

*'The child gives almost less trouble than an ordinary child of her age'. Janet
Winnie*

Young ones like the aforementioned were unfortunately more of a rarity or an
exception. Social and cultural expectations were very high. In order to maintain
reasonable levels of safety and to create a more socially acceptable environment
within the asylum walls, various patient behaviours seem to be in much need of major
modification. However, those misbehaving were still approached with some degree
of respect, for if they could not be held responsible for who they were, to what extent
could they be held responsible for their actions?

Some behaviours were not only unacceptable;
they were also at times very worrying and
causing much concern. The unsettled
conduct was at times caught at the very
beginning of treatment on the photograph
for admission. A couple of the new young
entrants were just not going to still for
the cameraman, and their images are
consequently quite blurred.

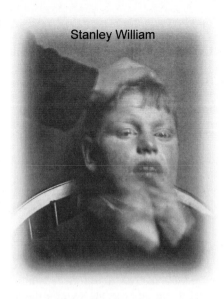

Stanley William

A couple of juvenile admissions had
performed quite dastardly deeds before
becoming asylum patients. Henry [1] had
stabbed his mother and William Christmas
had attempted to strangle his mistress
and had also threatened his mistress's
daughter with a carving knife. Fortunately,
the younger patients exhibited none of
these life threatening behaviours within the
asylum walls, with the exception of young
John William [1] whose drastic actions with
the ward kitten, denied it actually having the opportunity to become a cat, let alone
having its other eight lives.

Some like young Horace had their 'ups and downs', with quite rapidly interchangeable
moods, being 'either easily amused or easily upset.' Others had obviously developed
strong emotional reactions to the necessary care activities:–

> *'Throws herself on the floor and refuses to be touched... she always makes such a
> noise when interfered with'. Emma* [1]

It was obviously preferable if staff could work amongst contented faces but with patients
like James [1] in their midst this would be difficult as he appeared to only have one
mood:–

> *'Disposition is morose and is generally sullen and moody in his demeanour'.*

A youngster's frame of mind would obviously affect their actions, with epilepsy sadly
being a real provocateur. Several were noted for possessing quite violent tempers,
due to epilepsy. The adjective 'irascible' is in constant use throughout the case books.
Certain patients were not just 'mischievous' they were performing quite anti–social
acts. Betsy who had been relocated away from her family who lived in Leeds was 'rather
disposed to fight'.

It was unfortunate that it tended to be the more feeble or elderly patients, with whom
they shared treatment areas, who frequently suffered the inappropriate behaviours.
They were smacked, their feet were trodden on, their beards were pulled and their
chairs were pulled away from them just as they were about to sit down at the dining
table. The most serious misdemeanour was caused by Archibald:–

'Ran full tilt at an old man in the airing court - knocking him down causing a fracture of the femur and thigh'.

Some of the bad behaviours were basically just time wasting actions. These nuisance activities usually were related to various items of clothing like shoes, coats and waistcoats being continually taken off. Young Albert Isaac was described as one of the untidiest patients due to him never doing up his buttons.

The hyperactive also caused notable problems. Some would run up and down the galleries, or rush wildly about all day long. Fred was like "a small monkey continually clipping over any furniture." Many loved an official good run around the airing courts but John [2] was a little too over active:–

'Requires constant watching. He is constantly moving both his body and limbs and will not sit down. He takes little if any notice when spoken to'.

It was also preferable that the patients even with poor mental health or lower cognitive skills should be courteous, well mannered and conduct themselves in a socially acceptable way that was not viewed as being quite abhorrent to others. To the respectable adult the unacceptable behaviours appeared to show a complete lack of intellect and culture. The indecency of playing with genitals, or frequent masturbation was always discouraged often by adjustments to clothing from petticoats to trousers. Extra care was taken on bathing days to prevent the patients meddling with one another, particularly in the male section. Fred at the age of 13 was recorded in his case book records, for interfering with other men during the bathing sessions. It was not just actions that were carefully observed, their choice of language was also monitored too. Foul language always fell on highly critical ears. Many of those with severe learning difficulties had what appeared to be unacceptable modes of vocal interaction including the use of bad language:–

'Since admission patient has always been in a very irritable state and has resisted strongly any sort of interference. She is of very defective intelligence but is able to answer some questions and to articulate in a fairly distinct way although her vocabulary largely consists of foul language and oaths. She calls everybody some foul name and generally gets an adjective before most words especially if she is upset in anyway'. Violet Anne

Foul language was recorded in such a way, that the inappropriate language itself appeared to be viewed as a mental defect. George [6] was though credited with a fair level of intelligence because he had been able to use abusive language on several occasions. Elizabeth [4] had developed communication skills, which enabled her to swear quite fluently at the smallest trifle. Young Bertie was similarly recorded as he made 'incorrect statements'; showing himself to be a rather incoherent talker, he had though learnt to swear very freely. Several others were recorded as using either 'bad' or 'foul' language and this form of speech was always viewed as an exceptionally negative personal quality.

Frederick [1] admitted with simple mania had very strange speech patterns:–

'Is continually chattering incoherently, but certain words and sentences are repeated more than others viz - twenty one coconuts - Jack in the corner 21,21

- throw em up. Has a peculiar infantile voice - continually chattering certain sentences, the number 21 still occurs but he frequently puts in the word "bugger" when formerly he used no obscene language'.

It was not just spoken language that was judged to be somewhat inappropriate as was the case for Arthur [1]:

'Likes to sing one a song occasionally (his songs are invariably suggestive)'.

A few of the younger patients were recorded in performing acts of self–mutilation. John [1] was just recorded as being violent to himself and others. More details were provided for two other young male patients, with Thomas [1] being prone to hit his head with his hands, but George [5] caused himself more serious injury by knocking his head against a wall.

A few young ones rather than assaulting other patients were recorded as attacking asylum property instead. The cost of repairing or replacing various items resulted in them making noticeable holes in the asylum's actual finances. Albert Isaac and Alfred [2] were the cup breakers. Millicent was far more destructive with the crockery, with a tendency to suddenly, with one sweep of her arm, swipe all the cups and saucers within her reach. A couple of juveniles would like some of the adult patients; break the windows. The clothes–rippers would keep the women needle–working patients and tailors shop busy, as they were very destructive with their clothing. One lad William [2] was recorded as being:–

'Partial to stuffing the WC with whatever he can find'.

Duncan

Asylum property was damaged both indoors and out with young Duncan causing mayhem in the garden.

There is occasionally some information given on how any form of behaviour modification was attempted. In two 1st County Asylum medical journals[57] (the only ones still to be still extant), there are four columns for patients who are, or since the last entry have been, 'under restraint' or 'in seclusion', when and for what period, and reasons, and in the cases of restraint by what means. There are four columns within the Restraint– Seclusion section –One restraint column for males, one restraint column for females, one column for seclusion males, one column for seclusion females. Between 8th September 1873 and

4th April 1887 there are 32 cases recorded of patients (of any age) being required to be placed in seclusion. Mary Ann [1] was noted to have been put in a room for ½ an hour. Maria [2] admitted due to suffering from chronic mania in 1854, at the age of just 14, was obliged to be kept in her room occasionally. when she became over excited. One of the lads who was found 'misconducting himself with another male in the toilets' was, as a punishment, not allowed to go out to the farm as he usually did. Within these two journals there were no records of any form of restraint.

Some of those who were committing minor wrongs did not seem to be able to recognise that what they were doing was actually wrong. Fred was strongly spoken to about such things as stealing, getting out of windows or trespassing but the words appeared to have little if any affect on his actions.

'While witnessing a theatrical performance he employed himself in picking the patients pockets of tobacco and giving them to another patient the next day'. Fred

'His habits have been sedentary and anything but industrious, and his general conduct has been that of a youth young in his years, but old in crime'.William [7]

Many of the negative behaviours of those with deficient cognitive skills showed intelligence levels that did not coincide with their previously assessed mental abilities. For example mimicking other patients, required considerable powers of observation and dramatic performance. Transposing the words of a song to make them sexually suggestive also required a degree of intelligent and thoughtful composition (Arthur [1]). There were quite deep thought patterns within the feelings of jealousy, when other children were being given attention (Ida Elizabeth Mary). It was also problematic when Thomas [5] was constantly reporting attendants for striking him.

Thomas [5]

The most crucial part of any purposeful modification within treatment in the three asylums was how the patients were occupied during their days as patients. They were not wherever possible, left in a day–by–day straitjacket of the sameness of an asylum routine, valiant efforts were continually made to encourage better social skills and appropriately occupy the youngsters and this even included those who had initially been admitted as an 'incurable'.

Many of the young admissions were totally dependent on the assistance of others. A handful like Florence, Frederick [3] Lily and Beatrice needed absolutely everything to be done for them.

The development of certain patients with relatively weak basic personal skills, would not only save precious staff time, it would also enable young patients to become more confident and independent individuals. The lack of self-help skills was inevitably time consuming for staff, but it was not always viewed as a major individual negativity:–

> *'He is quite unable to dress himself or do anything much for himself, but otherwise gives no trouble at all'. Reginald William*

Florence

'A House of Cure and not a House of Detention'[58] was not only about nursing and curing mental illness it was also very much about nurturing any individual potential with the severely mentally impaired of any age. It cannot be overlooked that a high number of the patients were admitted as non-curable, who were going to essentially be virtual non-starters in any programmes for developing their personal skills.

> *'Makes no mental advance, is utterly incapable of education'. Ida Elizabeth Mary*
>
> *'Does not change at all'. Eunice*
>
> *'Intelligence not improved'. Arthur* [4]
>
> *'Appears to be incapable of any improvement'. Hilda*

Even though there is a fair degree of negativity in the previous inclusions, there are some even more tragically worded accounts of no progress in the case books for the patients:–

> *'Is making no headway - You might as well tack to a post'. Mary Beryl*

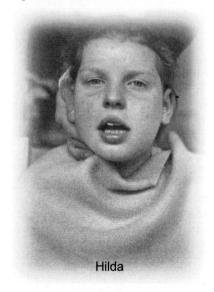

Hilda

---

58   Committee of Visitors Prefatory Remarks Rules 1849 Leicestershire's Lunatics H Orme and W Brock Leics Museums and Art Galleries Record Service 1987 ISBN 085022 2273.

'He continues a useless piece of human lumber'. William[4]

'Continues still alive –thin squalid feeble epileptic'. James [3]

'She is unoccupied except in disagreeing and interfering with others'. Mary Ann

Were these pessimistic phrases of those with a poor prognosis, borne out of the frustrations that came from over full asylums, which no longer had spaces for the cases that were potentially more curable?

Fortunately, in contrast to these harsh negativities, there were some successes noted in the individual case books, with regard to developing personal skills. William's [8] records on his admission in May 1878 read: –

'Incapable of dressing himself, has habit of destroying or hiding his clothes.
Is quite untrained in any useful habits'.

Within just two weeks he was recorded as learning to dress himself. Elizabeth [1] suffering from mania, eventually took a real pride in dressing herself too.

It was not just independence in dressing skills that needed to be concentrated on. Incontinence was continually recorded and only 23% of the under fourteen years olds admitted. were of 'clean habits'. The extent of the task is truly emphasized by the following case book entries

'Of dirty habits - His only delight is to dirty himself'.

'Has no control over his actions - inattentive to the calls of nature'.

'Habits are rather degraded and neglectful'.

'He obeys the call of nature just like an animal'.

'Passes evacuations unheeded'.

'Is very wet and dirty in her habits - Has to be changed many times a day'.

'Has some disagreeable habits after a room has been cleaned and swept she
will slip off if unobserved and pass urine and faeces in a corner of it. She has
frequently been confined to a chamber without result and soon after should any
opportunity occur would carry out this propensity'.

'He is much addicted to self pollution'.

'She has evidently been improperly brought up, not having been properly
corrected as to her dirty habits'.

'Spare habit of body'.

There were almost fifty young ones who were basically unclean in their toileting habits. Some of them were perhaps considered not to have had the mental capacity to be clean:–

'Is wet and dirty in habits. Continues wet and dirty and is practically devoid of intellect'.

Some of the entries for some of the cleaner 'idiots' almost imply that they had not been expected to be clean.

'So far she has been clean in her habits'. Eunice

'He must not be wet or dirty for so far he has been clean in his habits'. Albert

Just a few are recorded as needing a little assistance to remain clean and dry.

'She is clean in habits with attention'. Sarah Susan Ravina

'Is of neglectful habits unless tended carefully'. Mary [1]

'Is clean in her habits, does not wet the bed, but draws the attention to the nurse of her wants'. Elsie

Toilet training was therefore one of the most important activities that the staff were involved in with many of the young ones. Modification of weak personal habits resulted in less pressure for the already over–stretched staff, fewer articles of washing for the busy asylum laundries. The development of more acceptable personal skills also gave individuals greater pride in their own identity through their achievements. Quite a few of those who were initially recorded as being incontinent, made very noticeable improvements, which are recorded in their paperwork:–

Some of her dirty habits are ameliorated'. Harriett (four months after admission June 1864).

'Her habits are cleaner'. Mary [2] *(11 days after her admission).*

'Improvement in his personal habits'. James [1] *(2 months after his first arrival).*

'Is more cleanly under training'. Agnes (3 weeks after admission)

'Attends to her bodily wants much better than on admission'. Ann (2 months after becoming a patient).

'Is becoming gradually trained into more decent habits'. Mary [1] *(1 month after entry).*

Many of the younger patients being admitted for treatment, were at an age where they would have been attending a local school during the day. Asylum care was not only about nursing and curing mental illness it should surely also have been very much about nurturing any educational potential with the severely mentally impaired of any age. There is constant mention of scholastic ability or non–ability within the initial admission details: There is little if any mention of the young ones been given any opportunity to develop the three 'R's, even though on their admission, fastidious records were made of any abilities within this area. It is not mentioned if they were given access to books in the asylum library, or if the wards had a few which were more readily at hand There is though little if any mention of any scholastic educational activities within any asylum case book records. Only the following entries were found. (It is not clear if the entry for William [6] came within an ongoing assessment or if it was part of some basic educational programme): –

'The child is unable to speak but her hearing is very good and it is probable that she might be taught to talk a little'. Mary [2]

'Recognises and pronounces the names of animals, but is unable to answer questions'. William [6] *in 1888*

'Will do no work or settle to her letters. –Does not learn any new accomplishments'. Elizabeth [4]

No mention has been found on any form of school or teaching staff. There must though have been some form of educational focus, for it to be noted that a young 'idiot' girl Elsie was taking an interest in pictures.

Even though improvements were not necessarily immediate, the following records however outline some of the notable successes: –

a) 'She show no capacity for work and instruction' – 16 years later assisting in ward work. Millicent

b) 'Works well in whatever he is put to'. George [6]

c) 'Observes and is interested in pictures'. Elsie 1908

d) 'Sometimes shows slight intelligence'. Janet Winnie

e) 'He appears to understand better what is said to him'. John Samuel Clifford

f) 'Is much more orderly now in fact she began to mend after the first 4 days and has been steadily improving ever since'. Mary [3]

g) 'The child's health and habits are both materially improved she has left of spitting and obeys her nurse in many little matters'. Mary Ann [2]

h) 'Unable to speak except when using elementary words Mama and Papa'. Within several months there was a marked improvement in his speech and language skills:–'Trying to say fresh words and his vocabulary is growing – Says quite a lot of new words now'. Herbert a young 'idiot' admitted to the Borough Asylum in 1908.

When considering Herbert's speech and language skills one wonders if there truly was a much more positive attitude towards the educational potential of the severely mentally impaired within the asylum, than there was in the homes of certain of the individuals?

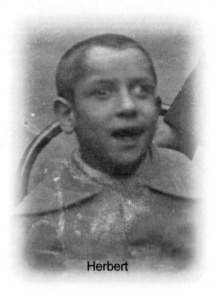

Herbert

Access to education was not a priority for the youth in the earlier decades of the 19th Century. For many their only schooling was gained at their weekly Church or Chapel attendances.

Details of the facilities for training can only be found between the lines of various other treatment details. There were many avenues of training in action to ensure that the youngsters became more acceptable patients within the asylum walls. At times behavioural patterns became quite intriguing. It is possible that some of the brighter kids may have manipulated situations so that they remained as patients.

Therapeutic Activities

The most significant part of any individual's asylum residency was the way they were able to spend their time and how therapeutic this would be for them. The way time was spent was dependant on both an individual's abilities and what actual activities were available to them.

The excerpts below come from the case books and emphasize the extent of the differences that the staff were faced with when planning long term leisure or occupational tasks for each individual young patient:–

> *'Harmless having childlike thoughts and pursuits…..Mental condition of a young child….is fond of toys plays with children'. Harriett*

> *'Works well at whatever he is put to'. George* [6]

> *'Much the same is difficult to amuse'. Elsie*

The extent of handicap in a few of the admissions had understandably resulted in a high degree of non–activity. They had though been admitted like any other patient for treatment and for these individuals it was potentially going to be quite a complex task, to find the best routes of progress. Several 'idiots' and one 'imbecile' were recorded as sitting in a chair all day:–

> *'Sits in a low chair and is practically helpless in it'. Lily*

> *'Sits in a chair all day and is carried out when weather permits'. Naomi Millicent*

> *'He has been seated in the open air when his health has permitted it'. Alfred* [2]

The absolute minimum of any available physical activity was for those who were sadly often virtually bedridden, was to be able to roll about in bed. Emily [2] an 'idiot' who had been admitted because of the way she had been so cruelly, but necessarily secured in her home. At the time of admission she was to be allowed to roll about freely on a bed upon the floor.

A few exhibited the basic mobility behavioural patterns of those with severe learning difficulties. With William [3] having ' the automatic sawing motion of body when sitting in a chair'. Cecil would perhaps get comfort by rocking himself to and fro. Some young patients would perform self–comforting rhythmic activities but it appears from an inclusion in Emma's [2] case book records that they were generally discouraged: –

> *'When permitted she sits on the floor swaying herself backwards and forwards'.*

The rocking repetitive rhythms could potentially be far more satisfying if it was accompanied by music. Young Henry [3] was recorded as remaining in the same place for hours at a time but he was fond of having music. William [5] was classified as one of the lowest 'idiots' possible, but he had some appreciation of music and time and would sway himself about with obvious delight if sung to.

They were not always indoors sitting in a chair, which was sometimes a special child's chair, with their objects of play. The long corridor–type wards allowed plenty of room for getting around, especially for those who were rather hyperactive. William [6] would run around making childish noises, playing with anything he could get hold of. Those who were recorded as rushing about wildly all day must have done most of that charging about indoors. One lad would though go into any room that he should not have been in, plus dangerously trying to clamber up shelves.

The Commissioners for Lunacy had various rules, that were expected to be complied with, and one of these, was that patients should have reasonable, regular access to the outside world. Part of their stipulations were that patients should have access to fresh air. The fresh air was almost certainly found within the safety of the locked airing courts.[59]. The outer walls could not have been that prolifically high, as several adult patients had successfully escaped over them. To be outside in the open air gave direct access to sunshine. William [8] in 1901 was recorded as going to sit in an armchair in the sunshine for a few hours.

Airing Courts

The airing courts were the official sites for exercise of any form. Bertie would walk about the court aimlessly, but young William [9] in contrast would be far more purposefully active whilst there.

---

59 The North West quadrangle of the Asylum, which would have been used as an airing court for female clients 1920's photograph
    – Photograph Courtesy of University of Leicester Archives

Four young ones named Duncan, Edgar William, Ida Winifred and Mabel loved to be chased about by members of staff and would laugh with pleasure during this active process. Elizabeth [4] was recorded as playing 'hide and seek' with the staff. For many a ball would be a major component in the courts. Some were far more advanced in their play skills with George [6] being quite able to amuse himself with a ball and Frances Anne Elizabeth would enjoy playing ball with other patients.

Those with more normal levels of intelligence would benefit from physical activities on the other side of the airing courts. Frederick [1] just three weeks after his admission would go with the adult walking parties, way beyond the grounds and sometimes right out into the surrounding countryside. The walks were not just a walk; they were often termed as 'promenades'. The female patients would take their walks in the morning and the males would take theirs after dinner. On 26th March 1875 – Good Friday 150 patients Borough Asylum went out walking. Fred in 1890 was continually asking to go out, giving the excuse that a fellow patient had promised him a job in the chimney sweeping business. One wonders whether any youngsters ever had a ride in the Small Japanese Carriage that Mr Thomas Cook presented to the Asylum for the use of the patients (30th March 1880). He also gave a short lecture on its history.[60]

As well as the walking activities, there were opportunities for more sporting types of pursuits. A couple of youngsters enjoyed playing a game of cricket in the evening. There may have been many supporters watching regular matches between adults from the Borough and County Asylums. For some ball games, cricket and billiards became not just casual time fillers, but much more strategic full time hobbies. Charles [2] took a deep interest in billiards and one young patient gained himself 2nd place in the asylum's billiard handicap

Whilst several loved playing with various types of ball, many of the younger ones needed opportunities for more imaginative play. The more fortunate were those who were capable of playing with toys in whatever location or physical position, as it was one of the priorities that they were found something to play with. The most common object of play was a doll and Harriett had been brought in a doll to play with. Ida Winifred also played with her doll.

Elizabeth [3] would play rather listlessly with dolls. Olive would play with a doll and its clothes, but was not able to do anything for herself with her own apparel. She was purposefully industrious in play but she could not transfer those skills towards self–help. (There are no records of males having been given access to a doll).

Ida Winifred

A young 'idiot' girl must have been very keenly observed, as it was noted that she loved to play with dolls, or anything bright that she was able to find. Maria Martha was also keen to get hold of a shiny watch chain. Mary [1] was absolutely delighted when somebody gave her a fan. Young hands enjoy being active and Ida Winifred would play for hours with a needle and cotton threading beads. John William [3] would constantly play with a spoon and Cecil liked to play with a bunch of keys, which he constantly jingled quite vigorously. Charles Percy would sit by the fire playing with two pegs, which he would pick up, and then throw down again.

Charles Percy

Others had intelligence enough to gain information on what toys there were to play with. William [8] had asked for a peg and top to play with. Had he seen the staffs' children on the outside playing with them? The staff acknowledged the need for children to have free access to play activities that a normal child would enjoy:–

> *'Is given to collecting things such as sticks in the garden and like many children makes her face and hands grubby'. Ida Winifred*

Activities during each day were sometimes dependent on the weather conditions. Gales brought down large iron windows (January 1884) and the Borough cricket pavilion (December 1909). In October 1877 a hurricane brought down one of the large stone pinnacles from the south front of the Borough female wing weighing several hundredweight. Snow and frost also caused difficulties – a late severe frost in February 1907 burst pipes in many different Borough wards, a glass veranda was broken during a large snow fall in February 1912. During May 1895 the weather became so cold that it was necessary to resume the fires. Better weather was far more warmly recorded. In May 1895 the evening dancing sessions were held out on the lawn. The following early April it was again so fine that hundreds of men went out on to the cricket field and a large number of female patients went out on to the croquet lawn.

One of the most social modes of play, particularly in childhood, was of course to have a playmate to play with. Mary [2] was specifically recorded as having another little girl about her size in the same ward 'who made a good play fellow for her' – (who must have been Elizabeth [1]). The only friend Albert Isaac would take in interest in was the asylum cat.

There were though other specific leisure activities recorded within the asylum records. Attendance to the Sunday service within the Asylum complexes was a very important part of the week, as patients would not have been denied the opportunity to follow their own religious faiths. Chapel attendances were usually only noted in the patient records if some misdemeanour had occurred whilst there. There were only two records found within the case books of a younger patient attending one of the asylum chapels. One of them was the young music lover Archibald who liked chapel, when there was a choral service, but he did not enjoy morning prayers. He was on admission recorded with 'none' for his religion. At least he was given opportunities to have access to religious activities within the asylum.

The more musical activities within the chapel proved to be very therapeutic to the patients in general. Another lad also much enjoyed going to any choral services held in the chapel. The singing of hymns was usually a favourite part of any service. . One of the most annoying after effects of this section of worship was that many who could remember some of the words and the tunes, would spend all day singing them, leading to those in their immediate company becoming significantly disturbed. Jane [2] admitted with epileptic mania, was one who 'could easily recall her favourite hymns and would annoy the other patients by singing them at the top of her voice.' In April 1862, in the 1st County Asylum it was decided to commence singing and chanting a portion of the service, the results were twofold. Firstly, the behaviour of the congregation became remarkably good and secondly a very large proportion of the patients ended up grinning during the responses. [61] Non–conformist services were also held in the Asylum Chapels.

It was not only the Sunday chapel services that were a musically linked entertainment provider for the asylum patients of any age. There were various other leisure activities arranged too. One of the most significant arrivals at the 1st County Asylum was the gift of a French Piano in or around 1846. The instrument enabled the resident medical officer, to establish dancing twice a week, which he believed, assisted him considerably in his curative measures. Several of the younger patients with learning difficulties are recorded at the 1st County Asylum of being allowed to go the other entertainments and weekly balls. Some would quite enjoy themselves sitting and enjoying the music or just dancing alone at dances or at the weekly ball when there was one.

> *'Enjoys the dances sits swaying his body or rocking his head forward to the rhythm of the music'.*

In February 1865 there is reference to a weekly ball in one of the patients case notes[62]. They did of course have to behave themselves, but Elizabeth [1] in 1867 who went to the

---

61 1st County Superintendent's Journal DE3533–84
62 1st County Asylum Case Book Records. DE3533–191–2578

weekly ball 'always conducted herself in a very orderly manner'. Some like Ida Winifred, would be extremely disappointed if they did not go to the ball or other entertainments. Emily's [1] non existent language skills did not hold the staff back from sending her to share the fun:–

> *'Cannot speak a word - likes to come to all the entertainments'.*

Another young lad had similar mental abilities to Emily [1], but the staff did not let limited abilities result in patients like them, missing out on various potentially enjoyable, therapeutic activities.

In March 1906 Sir Tollemache Sinclair presented the Borough Asylum with a gramophone, which was for the use of the patients.

> *'The gramophone that was presented to the Asylum has been working satisfactorily for some weeks past and the patients find it very amusing'. April 30th"*[63]

In January 1911 the numbers of patients for the Borough Asylum were 291 males and 361 females. There were 322 patients who went to the previous Christmas entertainments[64], leaving 330 as actual 'non–eventers.' Did the non–attendees get the same much–appreciated seasonal gifts as those who went to the celebration?

---

63   Borough Superintendents Journal VI DE2853– 45
64   Photograph of County Asylum Recreation Room at Christmas Stewart Collection Courtesy of Leicestershire, Leicester and Rutland Record Office.

The Asylum Superintendent's Journals and Diaries are overflowing with entries of various performers, with names and dates of the presentations. The Superintendents themselves end up becoming virtual entertainment managers. All the asylums eventually had their own stages within recreation rooms, with a piano by then being accepted as an exceptionally necessary item of furniture.

There were theatrical performances within the Asylums themselves, usually in the recreation rooms. Various amateur dramatic groups, or members of staff put together plays, burlesques or pantomimes, much to the intrigue and enjoyment of their patients. Minstrel groups, schools and several Church and Chapel Choirs sang glees (musical compositions for three or more voices) or other songs. Drum and pipe bands came to play and a celebrated harpist named Mr Aptommas came to perform. Ultimately both asylums managed to put together their own bands from staff and patients. Ventriloquists, comedians and conjurers also arrived to perform. In January 1891 the St Marks and Belgrave Gymnasium Clubs gave entertainment. Most of the performers must have been of reasonable quality, as many returned several times.

There were also lectures on Heavenly Bodies and on various wonders in Earth and Sea, illustrated by a magic lantern. In 1876 the 'Leicester Dissolving Views Company' put on a show for the patients. A couple of decades later (February 1897) a Mr Bertini arrived to give an exhibition of a kinematograph by means of lime light – About a dozen pictures were thrown on the screen and the patients really enjoyed the novelty of the performance. Dr Rothsay Stewart was one of the Superintendents who travelled the world in his vacations. A month or so after his return he would present a lantern slides show, with slides taken in Spain. Portugal, Budapest, Switzerland, Canada. Vienna, Florence, Rome, Bruges, Gloucester and Norwich. . In December 1909, the London Bioscope Company arrived to offer patients an early form of cinema. In Oct 1896 Mr Elliott's Minstrel Company, was the only arranged entertainment, that was recorded as failing to put on an appearance, in many decades of visiting entertainers.

There is no indication of times of day that various performances took place: There are also no details on which age group of patients had access to them. Did the children though have an opportunity to watch the Punch and Judy Shows? One adult patient was recorded as helping get the boys to bed; there is no mention of actual bed times. Certain entertainment activities may have conflicted with the sleeping timetables. Occasionally, unexpected occurrences, both positive and negative, led to entries related to attendance at certain entertainments being entered in certain patients case books. 'Fred was at the age of 12, going to the theatrical performances and employing himself picking pockets.

Some patients had the opportunity to participate in certain entertainments on the outside. There were the seasonal assemblages of the more industrious patients on the front lawns for dancing, bowls, quoits and other popular sports. Thanks to the kindness of the lessees over a hundred patients would go to watch the annual pantomimes, which took place at the Leicester Theatre Royal or the Opera House. Tickets or free passes were also given for patients to visit Leicestershire Agricultural Show held on the Race Course or an Exhibition at the Floral Hall. On 19th June 1869 'the proprietors of Henry and Adams Circus invited the patients to witness their exhibition and 75 of the more orderly patients were enabled to avail themselves of this invitation'.[65] A few of the

---

65   1st County Superintendent's Journal DE3533–85

younger admissions presented behaviour patterns that sadly could hardly be described as anything near 'orderly'.

The most notable entry in the 1st County Asylum's Superintendent Journals was an absolutely incredible, totally amazing, picnic recorded at the Newton Unthank Asylum farm 13th June 1883. The 1881 Census, confirms just how close the Asylum Farm was for rail access, as next door to the farm, lived the Gateman for the Midland Railway and his neighbour was the Railway Pointsman: –

> '....we reached a kind of climax yesterday when, with the knowledge of Mr Woodcock we held a monster picnic and some 350 of the Patients and staff were taken to the Farm at Newtown Unthank by a Special train from the Welford Road Siding - The train left at 1.p.m. and returned from Desford at 7.p.m. The party were supplied with tea, cake, bread and butter and cold meat at about ½ past three in the afternoon. The Patients were seated in two separate Camps; the sexes apart. A Large tent, which had been leant to us kindly by Mr Billson, Belgrave Rd was erected in case of rain; and we took our attendants band of music - The day was everything that could be desired; the Party behaved very well, and all apparently enjoyed themselves immensely - Not a single mishap or unpleasantness occurred - Mr H C Woodcock honoured us for an hour in the afternoon. We all reached home safely at 7.30 pm very thankful at having completed our anxious undertaking and at having carried through to a successful issue what I think may be considered as quite an unprecedented excursion. The success of the undertaking was due in great measure to the fact that our Station at Welford Road siding was so close to the Asylum (being only 200 yards distant) and is so private. Secondly to the possession of our own Estate at Newtown to picnic upon - Finally, the patients were extremely manageable, perhaps because during the last 6 months, they have been allowed so much liberty and have been so little locked up'. Reported in journal entry dated 13th June 1883[66]

This grand picnic happened again in July 1884. Within the 1st County Asylum's Superintendent's Journals is another remarkable piece of information. The words are just slotted in amongst the other entries, with nothing within the script to make them stand out from the rest, except for what they were saying: –

> 'Nevertheless on the 2nd inst in the afternoon, Not one male patient was in bed, in the wards, or even in the airing courts - That is every individual male patient was free and beyond lock and key - and it may be doubted whether this ever occurred before in any Asylum'. June 1885 [67]

It cannot be ascertained if the Superintendent was only referring to adult males but in the month of June 1885 Edward and Thomas [8] were both grown up aged 36, one William [8] was 21 but John William [1] was aged just 7 and another William [2] was 10 years old. Were these individuals, some of them just children, part of the males who were all out and about somewhere? Wherever and whenever possible the hours spent, as a young asylum patient, many years ago was time well spent.

66   County Superintendent's Journal DE3533–86
67   County Superintendent's Journal DE3533–87

Work Based Opportunities

An individual's occupation was one of their most important roles within their immediate communities and acquiring a trade was an absolute 'must'. Many of the young individuals outside the walls were taking up apprenticeships, which sometimes involved them having to live away from home. Records for previous schooling and or any occupation held, may have affected attitudes towards their employable potential within the asylum.

The age for commencement of any occupation was much younger in these earlier years and several of the younger admissions were noted with a former occupation within the appropriate entry box of their admission case book sheet. Several of those who were mentally ill at the time of admission had previous occupations, usually in domestic service of some form. Their life must have been dramatically affected – Firstly by their mental illness, secondly by their admission to an asylum in Leicestershire, thirdly to be no longer spending their days at work and fourthly to be looked after and well fed.

One of the most important roles that the asylums could play within a treatment programme, was to continue to give patients of almost any age, or ability, something important to do or a job of some form: The majority of them had reached physical maturity and it was crucial therefore that they should be purposefully active. The hours in the day were not all usually free to relax in, as this was not the rhythm of normal life. A high percentage of individuals were therefore given tasks that were significant enough, for their activities to be termed as an actual occupation. Wherever possible total respect was afforded to each of their interests and capabilities. William [10] though had little interest in anything beyond the hoarding of his money: –

> 'He says he will not do any work because he is not paid for it'.

It was not going to be possible to find those with more severe learning difficulties tasks within the asylum. Elizabeth [4] was tragically noted in January 1896 as being:–

> 'Quite unoccupied (that is from a point of usefulness)'.

Mercifully, several of those, with minimal mental capacities from birth, were able to make themselves useful within the daily routines of the Asylum. The priority was to get the patients who were well enough into daily working routines. It was almost always a case of someone eventually being tried out and assessed with an indoor task before they were given an opportunity to work outdoors. One major problem when employing patients of any age with learning difficulties would be that they would not be able to sustain their attention, on any task they were given. A high level of supervision was therefore often required to keep the young patients actually focused on the assignment. Some, whose health could vary, would work indoors when they were frail (often due to epilepsy) and outdoors when they were physically stronger.

Remissions and various individual 'ups and downs' were well catered for. If a young patient was temporarily under the weather, perhaps due to epilepsy, then they were given less arduous tasks until they were well again, but they generally still had something to do. Even those who were not fully continent like James [2] would be allowed to be employed out on the farm.

The condition of epilepsy was not viewed as a 'no go area'. Individuals would remain employed regardless of whether they were epileptic or not. Generally, epileptic patients would be offered the same opportunities within daily life at the Asylum. Many would go to the farm or work in the grounds. Ultimately, one of the most tragic effects of the fits was for a patient to lose their employment as a member of the Asylum work force.

Several of those patients aged fourteen and under are positively noted to be assisting in some form of ward work. For some particularly the girls, it was encouragement to learn basic hands skills such as sewing. One of the girls Elizabeth [1] is recorded as:–

'She occasionally does a little needle work'.

It was not just hand skills within a chair, there were also many, more active, basic, daily chores that the patients of all ages, would assist with, in the wards. The adult patients frequently have the tasks they performed, specified within their records – dusting, watering the flowers, laying the tables, cleaning boots, helping the more frail to the table, making beds. Millicent who was admitted at the aged 11 had her first mention of ward work, at the age of 28. She was when not in a too 'cantankerous frame of mind able to assist with scouring'. George [4] in 1903 was able to make himself useful in a small way by cleaning boots. There were very few entries with specifically named indoor tasks found in the younger patient records of all three asylums. For both sexes, it was a case of making themselves 'useful indoors' or doing 'ward work' or doing 'household work'. It was mainly the 'imbeciles' and those suffering from simple manias that were doing this type of task. Most of this group were recorded as doing ward tasks at the same age as when they were admitted. One 'imbecile' named Thomas [8] who was initially admitted as a twelve–year–old ' was 33 years old, before he had any record included of ward work. Bertie an 'imbecile' in April 1909 believed himself to be a very strategic member of staff within an asylum ward:–

'Very simple, has little sense: thinks he is a ward attendant'.

Patients of any age could not just turn up for a position of employment within the Asylum. The Matron and Chief Attendant would have to know where places were available, and they would then have to discuss with the head of the work location, if they were willing to take on certain individual patients. The 'head' was usually an outsider specifically employed by the asylums in certain work areas. The four most likely places for the young to be employed were in the wards, the laundry, the gardens or the farm.

A considerable percentage of the juvenile patients were actually quite physically fit and ready for the great outdoors. Frederick [1] with simple mania was successfully cured quite quickly, but there is surprisingly no record of him participating in any tasks out in the fresh air. The 1st County Asylum, initially selected the outdoor tasks, which were in close proximity to the main complex, rather than taking greater risks in the seven–mile distant farm at Newtown Unthank, with a much lower staff ratio. With the exception of those suffering from severe epileptic mania, almost all the mentally ill younger patients were found suitable industrious asylum activities.

The least likely to be given any form of employment were those defined as 'idiots'. Safety issues have to be considered, but just one 'idiot' was found with an occupation in the asylum records. He was Henry Simon who suffered from epilepsy too:–

'Works in the wards does not alter - Is idiotic but manages to help in the ward work'. Jan 21ˢᵗ 1904

A juvenile patient named James [2] had been classified as an 'idiot', until he went to work on the farm when he was given 'imbecile' status instead. Those with lower mental abilities were not necessarily permanently signed off.

James [2]

The age when the young patients commenced appropriate employment can be approximately gauged from some of the case book inclusions. Twelve years is the youngest age found in the records, for a patient assisting in any way during their period of treatment. George [4] was boot cleaning; Arthur [6] had been out to work on the Borough Farm (which was on site), whereas Alfred [1] at the age of just 13 was working at the Newtown Unthank Farm, which was 7 miles distant from the 1ˢᵗ County Asylum.

By the age of 14 (as those listed below), it appears that they must have been truly considered as grown up, with then higher expectations of their occupational abilities:–

Mary Ann [1] with simple mania – 'Can make herself useful'

James [2] an 'idiot' – Worked at the Borough farm

Edmund an 'imbecile' – Worked in the County Asylum gardens or out at the farm

Charles [2] with dementia – Worked in the gardens

Charles [3] with primary dementia – Worked in the stables and gardens

Thomas [7] with mania – Worked in the upholstery shop

Thomas [6] with simple mania –Worked in the ward

For the females of any age, the only actual asylum occupations given were found indoors, in the wards, galleries, kitchens, sculleries or laundry. There was so much to be done in the laundry and it was an incredible hive of hot, hard work for both the asylum staff and the patients. Not all the patients could cope with the heat that was emitted from the laundry. Some of the young girls were though able to handle it very well. Annie regardless of her fits, was still able to go to the wash house. By July 1898 ventilating fans are mentioned in the Borough Asylum laundry and they must have been there for some time, as they needed fixing.[68] It is obvious that the management have made very genuine attempts to improve working conditions.

Several of the younger teenage girls were quickly allocated a placement in the laundry or the 'wash house'. One of the slightly older teenagers with learning difficulties, named Ruth, just loved working in the laundry: –

> *"Works industriously at Wash House and delights in getting wet through at all times of the year."* October 1885 [69]

Several of the older patients, requested to work in the washroom or were tested out there, but were just not physically well enough to be there. The fact that several of the young ones managed to be successfully employed there, truly emphasizes how physically well many of them were

The fit young males would be sent outdoors. No records were found of the females working outside, with the exception of an adult female taking up the role of gate keeper. The phrase 'to the farm' is a continually written within the surviving casebook records for the male of any age at both asylums. The asylum patients became almost like a more normal farmer's extended family. As more serious disruption was possible in the highly skilled workshops, the younger ones were generally sent to the farm where they may have been less likely to cause any damage or disruption:–

> *"Remains in the same demented state. Gives no trouble and works well on the land."* Isaac Feb 1909

Several young males went out to either the Borough Farm, which was virtually on site, or to the 1st County Asylum farm, which was 7 miles distant at Newton Unthank. Some Borough youngsters are recorded as arriving, but not actually doing anything once they had arrived:–

> *'He does little work but goes out to the farm everyday'.* Thomas [3]

Case book entries like this are very impressive, as they are direct evidence of the patients still being given an opportunity, both to gain an experience within an agricultural occupation and a chance to be in another potentially productive environment for the day, regardless of how behaviourally disruptive, epileptic, inactive or incontinent they were. Arthur's [6] fits at intervals were severe in character, but he still worked at the Borough Farm.

It was not just the 'imbeciles' who were given days out at the farm. Those with far less intellectual capacities, the 'semi idiotic' and 'virtual idiots' went too. The casebook records for

Arthur [6]

Thomas [3] are very inspiring with their details:–

> *"He is still employed as a wheeler and is always very childish." 1889 Sept 12th*

> *"Is generally cheerful and fond of sky larking." 1890 March 19th*

> *"Is in the same idiotic state but able to go on the farm. Is partially idiotic and works on the farm. July 1897*

> *"Very demented - has no idea of place and time - quite incoherent in speech - employed on farm in Good Health." 1910 Nov 15th*

The employment of the youngsters out on the asylum farms must not all be viewed as negative skylarking with a wheelbarrow. George [6] worked well on the farm after absolutely refusing to become a tailor or shoemaker. Another Charles[70] was soon given a position on the asylum farm, where he was always worked very well, cheerfully singing or whistling whilst he laboured away and was exceptionally skilled at chopping wood.

The farm also inadvertently provided one of the best avenues for the great escape, which came by being employed at the farm in the day, preferably when it was very foggy. Several adults made successful illegal exits via the farms, but just one younger patient Thomas [6], absconded in this way, at lunch time in October 1888: –

There are many more entries of the young ones working well on the farm. They must have been proud to be part of such a successful farm community, as a great proportion of the 'daily fare' at the asylums was 'home grown'. They would have helped to cultivate many varieties of potato such as Early Rose, Myatts, Magnums, Champions or Ash Leaf. The youngest may have also helped to cultivate kidney or broad beans, peas, cabbages, broccoli, kale, cauliflowers, carrots, turnips, Swedes, onions, parsnips, mangolds and various types of fruit. The production line at the 1st County Asylum was so successful that any surplus produce was sold by auction on Saturday mornings.

The juvenile assistants may have also assisted in looking after the asylum livestock. In October 1883, the records list the stock on the 1st County Asylum farm as 30 sheep with 13 lambs, 10 theaves (*female sheep*), 6 ewes with 1 ram and finally 84 pigs including 9 sows and 1 boar. There was frequent record of the Harvest Festival celebratory meals enjoyed by approximately 70 to 80 of the farm–working patients, but there are again no details of the age of the patients who participated in this annual feast. In 1896 at one of the harvest meals, they enjoyed 'pork pie, jam tarts, cheese and celery, with a smoking concert being held afterwards.'[71]

Just like the male farm workers with their annual harvest celebration the females who worked in the kitchens and laundry at the 1st County Asylum also had a yearly treat. For them it was a summer day out and picnic usually on a week day at Bradgate Park. In June 1875 fifty five females went out, but no records have survived as to exactly who enjoyed this summer outdoor feast and whether it included any of the younger patients, but from the records Elizabeth [1] could well have gone with the group.

---

70   DE3533–193–3217 1st County Asylum Case Books
71   DE2853–65 Borough Superintendent's Diary

As well as working out on the farm they worked out in the stables. It was a patient working with a carter that stopped a new carthorse bolting when it was startled by a motorcar in May 1901. There were several other jobs to assist with outside. Alfred [1] admitted with mania had, among many other occupations, a spell outdoors helping the painter.

Another work area frequently mentioned, for the boys, was the asylum gardens. Especially for the County Asylum the gardens, which were adjoining and not like the farm, seven miles down the road. Young Charles [2] was noted to take an interest in gardening.

Charles [2]

Asylum Gardens

In the gardens there was much to be done. There is even mention of a 'cucumber house' in May 1910 at the Borough Asylum, being pulled down and rebuilt. Considerable levels of therapy must have been found in the knowledge that you were a successful part of a team that kept up the asylums farms and the beautifully landscaped surroundings.[72]

---

72   Photograph of 1st County Asylum Gardens and Fielding Johnson Building Courtesy of University of Leicester Archives ULA/ FG1/3/10

Skills would be gained working in the wards, sculleries, kitchen, laundries, at the farm, stables, with the carters or in the gardens. More complex skills could be gained working in the asylum workshops. During the early years of the 1st County Asylum there was no such opportunity.

> *'10/1/1854 It is much regretted that the want of workrooms in the Asylum does not permit that general employment by the patients in such occupations as shoemaking, tailoring ... and stocking weaving - occupations which while they are normal in other County Asylums are to be regarded as a great means to curative treatment'.* [73]

Once more workshops were constructed or included, selected employment as an integral part of treatment within the asylum, became easier to allocate. Only those patients with relatively, balanced behaviours and a reasonable degree of intelligence, would be the ones who would be fortunate enough to gain a place in these asylum–workshops, which were run by skilled members of various trades who had been employed as outsiders.

It must never be overlooked that the asylums primary aim was for it to be a 'A House of Cure' its secondary aim was for the shops to be productively successful: –

> *'1/1/1855 During the past year the employment of the Patients has considerably increased, the boots and shoes worn by them are made and repaired in the Asylum as is also the Clothing of the Male and Female patients with few exceptions'.* [74]

> *'12/6/1872 The stock of clothing made up in the store rooms appear to be sufficient for ordinary consumption of the asylum for at least 6 months. I have therefore employed the tailor in cleaning and restuffing the bed mattresses - and he with some 5 or 6 male patients is engaged upon this work in the new workshops'.* [75]

It is understandable therefore that those who were liable to be less productive, were not fortunate in getting a place in the highly skilled shops. Patients of any age with more seriously maladapted, excitable behaviours, were liable to damage either shop equipment or the goods and to subsequently cause disorder on the production line.

Once the workshops had been constructed very few of the young admissions gained places within them. Those with the most promise for the future were sadly probably, usually the 'curable' youngsters. William [10] and Thomas [4], eventually worked in the horsehair and upholstery shop, together with George [6] who had absolutely refused to be a tailor or shoemaker. Alfred [1] was admitted twice, firstly as an 'imbecile' and secondly with 'mania'. (He had previously been a golf caddy and was continually up and down both physically and mentally). A couple of years following another relapse he recovered and was successfully taught to work very successfully in the 1st County Asylum bakery.

---

73 1st County Superintendent's Journal DE3533–83
74 1st County Superintendent's Journal DE3533–83
75 1st County Superintendent's Journal DE3533–85

Alfred [1]

There are two teenage Borough Asylum patients, whose first case book admission records have not survived, but there are continuation records of their treatment in later case books. The inclusions are a clear statement of the range of opportunities that were given to patients in the Leicestershire Asylums regardless of their age, ability, or the potential dangers they faced or caused on site: –

Samuel

'Is in the same childish state with a very high opinion of his own abilities.

Is employed with the Bricklayer and gives little trouble.1896 Feb 16th to 1899 July 7th

1899 Oct 2nd employed as stoker

1901 Jan 4th Works with the engineer.

1901 Oct 26th Working with engineer

1901 May 31 Partially imbecile

1904 Oct 25th Is childish and unable to articulate properly, works with the engineer. Troublesome at times

1906 May 9 Works well at engine house Vol H Page 151

1907 May 19th Got scorched in the Engine House yesterday, got his arm and face burned slightly

1911 Nov 10th Employed at old boiler house

1911 May 14th Patient got slightly scorched on face as the result of a back draught in the old boiler house.'

Edward[76] was aged 16 when he arrived as a patient and he worked in a similar environment to Samuel, as a helper in the boiler house with the stoker. He was given the same opportunities as Samuel and regardless of his poor behaviour patterns, he was still allowed the opportunity to perform industriously: –

'1899 March 20th Works well with stoker

1899 July 8th He left the Boiler House with the supposed object of going to the Cricket Field and was not afterwards seen.

1899 July 9th Patient was brought back to the Asylum this evening. He had been wandering about the country all night and returned to his friends in the evening.

1901 May 20th He works well in the Boiler House. Is occasionally troublesome and destructive

1905 Oct 29th Working well with the Engineer and not giving any trouble. Remains childish and facile. Is a useful man in the boiler house'.

Those allocating occupational placements did therefore focus on the young ones potential. Priority was always given to individuals having experience within a trade and being therapeutically employed in something, when it was safe for them to do so.

Various behavioural programmes had also been implemented too within the three asylums to encourage both safety and independence skills. Several patients had enough cognitive capacity or potential, to become like many others, a part of the asylum work force. The asylums were though far more financially viable, with the patients being part of the work force and the young ones were part of the team.

---

76   Borough Asylum Case Book Records DE2853–178–77 and DE2853–179–80

The Outcome of the Treatment

What was the eventual outcome of all the staff efforts given to the one hundred and thirty seven under fourteen year old asylum admissions? Within the case book records there are both negative and positive inclusions in an attempt to effect improvements.

The most incredible record of asylum treatment, for the very young comes with Frederick [1] admitted with simple mania in 1891. This is a case book inclusion just 3 weeks after his admission:–

> *'He is now much quieter goes beyond the grounds for walks, answers questions rationally and asks to be allowed to go home. Has been to the entertainments and enjoyed them'.*

The aforementioned entry, highlighting an exceptionally rapid recovery, was very rare for patients of any age. The records were often of more negative content, with many giving details of young lives ending on an asylum death–bed. The cause of death or the death certificate is not always part of the case book records, but for those where the specific reason is included almost twenty died from epileptic convulsions and almost forty died from some form of infectious lung conditions. Humbling environmental conditions, prior to admission may have already weakened many of the children and they were therefore very susceptible to any diseases spread by contagion such as phthisis (tuberculosis), both inside and outside the asylums.

Degeneration during treatment

There were considerable variations in the eventual outcomes for the young asylum admissions. There are far more depressing individual histories, than more encouraging ones. The long–term prospects for many of those admitted to an asylum in childhood were inescapably bleak, through no fault of the treatments within the asylums.

Within the medical records, there are entries, which emphasize patterns of very noticeable degeneration within those who grew up and grew into old age within the asylum walls. Some were noted 'to be going slowly down hill'. In certain cases, the long term employment opportunities, could be considered to be far from positive, if their status of being technically unable to be cured at the time of their admission is forgotten. Those who were able to remain within their families may also have had depressing long term work opportunities on the outside. Several juveniles did become virtually inactive, unoccupied and very degenerate. One of the accounts of a life within the asylum walls comes with George [6] the 'imbecile' from Loughborough who in his youth would jump on a train without a ticket. At the age of fourteen he was a keen football player within the asylum and worked both in the horse hair shop or out on the farm. The record of him 20 years later (still as a patient) emphasizes a considerable degeneration, (allowing for the fact that six months after this entry he has died from the dreaded phthisis)':–

> *'A lazy stout imbecile man will not move or walk a yard, unless compelled and he never attempts to employ his time even by looking at a book'.*

Broad statistics of outcomes

If all age groups were included, the 1st County Asylum had the statistical success of 50% cured or relieved enough to return to former lifestyles.[77] In contrast only 7% of the under fourteen year olds were cured in this asylum. A high proportion of the 137 (from all 3 asylums) who were aged 14 and under at the time of admission did not therefore experience good future prospects:–

107 Died in an asylum

6 were relocated in other county asylums in Derby, Northampton and Worcester, as it was a general policy that patients should be treated in their own initial settlement areas and they too may have died in an asylum

5 were discharged

12 recovered or were relieved

7 remained as longer–term patients

Those who recovered

The youngsters who were recorded with recovery are listed below:–

George [1] admitted with Chronic Mania recovered after 3 months

Mary [3] admitted with Sub Acute Mania recovered after 3 months

Charles [2] admitted with Dementia recovered after 5 months

Charles [3] admitted with primary dementia recovered after 4 months

Alfred [3] admitted with Epileptic Mania recovered after 6 months

Arthur [5] admitted as an imbecile recovered after 6 months

Edmund admitted being deficient in mind from Leicester Prison after running off with a horse and trap for a joke. After several trials at home he was eventually successfully relocated there after 8 months.

Frederick [1] following a readmission with simple mania, recovered after 6 months

Walter admitted with Mania recovered after 2 years.

Louisa admitted with Melancholia recovered after 6 years

Thomas [7] admitted with mania recovered after 4 months.

Mary Ann [1] after a readmission with simple mania recovered after 6 months.

Some with congenital birth defects, who could technically not be cured, may have only had their behavioural standards improved, but a few of them went home in just a few months. Only 6 young 'idiot' or 'imbecile' patients were recorded as going home again

77   Leicestershire's Lunatics – The Institutional care of Leicestershire's Lunatics during the Nineteenth Century H G Orme W H Brock Leicestershire Museums and Art Galleries 1987 ISBN 085022 227 3

or to 'friends' (who may not have been their immediate family) within an average time of 6 months.

Discharged not improved

A few may have returned home again after they had been considered well enough to do so and stayed there: Some though like Naomi Millicent, Muriel and Joseph Montague were discharged 'not improved'. Walter James was also released in the same condition with his 'friends' promising to look after him. A return home was not necessarily the best route for a patient to take:–

> *'Since her removal, for she has been kept in a dark cellar, chained to a post - the fear and tenor of the neighbourhood'. Emma* [2]

Relocation to other asylums

For some on the move, it was not in the homeward bound direction, but just relocation to another asylum. This relocation was almost always because they were being moved to the asylum, sited nearest to where they were directly chargeable. Once the new Borough Asylum opened, three young Leicester patients – Millicent, Edith and Sarah were all relocated there. For George [6] it was a move in the opposite direction from the Borough Asylum to the 1st County Asylum. Elizabeth [1] was relocated to the Berrywood Asylum in Northamptonshire. Cecil William aged 4 and Thomas [1] aged 6, were also relocated to this asylum after 1887. From this date there had been building extensions, which created a new specific block for 'idiot' and 'imbecile' children adjacent to the female wing. George [4] had one of the farthest relocations to Worcester Asylum, but this was almost certainly because this was his original place of birth, or settlement area, who would be paying the expenses of treatment. When the 1st County Asylum became desperately over full in the 1890's, several places were found at Beverley Asylum in Yorkshire. Mary [1] and Edward were Leicestershire asylum patients, so they went to Beverley, just like any other Leicestershire asylum patient who was able to be temporarily relocated.

Deaths within the asylum

The fact that 117 never returned home, many of them passing away within the asylum walls, is a tragically high proportion of those who were admitted to the asylums of Leicestershire many years ago, at a very young age. The figures would potentially have been even more alarming, if those whose records were missing or incomplete were included too. Sixteen of the young patients died within a year of being admitted. Willie aged just five years and Elizabeth [3] aged 12 both died within a month of admission, one from tubercular phthisis and the other from tubercular meningitis. Willie who died within a month of a tubercular lung condition, was recorded as being 'in bed' on admission and was perhaps understandably, tragically quite accurately described 'a wretched looking little creature'. . He may have come from a bed at home and was placed straight into an asylum bed in the 1st County asylum. The majority of the case book pages for the young admissions, sadly, ultimately have a death certificate attached to them.

For those who died, not all of the causes of death are recorded, but some of the causes other than epilepsy and infectious lung conditions are given as abscesses in liver and cerebellum, cerebral congestion, influenza, anaemia, bronchitis, burns, spinal caries and myelitis, disseminated sclerosis, typhoid, cirrhosis of liver, meningitis and pneumonia. Just over 30 of them are recorded as dying in the asylum after 2 years.

Growing up in an asylum

The greatest gift that a treatment period within an asylum could offer, was to be given an opportunity to safely grow up, this was often not possible within their own homesteads due to open fires and open doors. If the age of seventeen is taken as an average age for reaching adulthood, then 61 of the 137 studied grew up in the asylum. Eighteen of that number died in their later teenage years whilst still a patient and another eleven passed away in their twenties. Many of those with some form of mania, melancholia or dementia were usually cured relatively quickly and would therefore have been able to complete their growing up back in the outside world.

Many young patients, who had congenital mental problems or were recorded as having had defects from birth, were probably not going to be cured, even though behaviours could be noticeably improved. Those who grew up in the asylum were usually those who did not suffer from other clinical problems such as epilepsy. Elizabeth [4], an 'imbecile' who had initially admitted at the age 10 had ten years later really grown up. She was then able to convert her appearance into that of a young lady: –

> 'Is getting to be a strong girl - Has now put her hair up and takes all the tucks out of her dress to lengthen it and considers herself a grown up woman (Aged 20 then). Is as boisterous and childish as ever, works in the laundry'. January 1902

Alfred [1] was admitted at the age of 13, but four years later, when still an asylum patient, he had similar life ideals to adults on the outside. He was employed out of doors with the painter and mentioned that he would like to be playing golf.

Long stay patients

The average period of treatment before death for all those who died is approximately eleven years. However, taking the age of death as a group statistic, covers up some horrendous life figures for a few of the young admissions who ultimately died within asylum walls in old age: –

Harriet admitted at the age of 10 dies after 51 years aged 61

William [10] admitted at the age of 10 dies after 57 years aged 67

Edward admitted at the age of 12 dies after 57 years aged 69

Samuel admitted at the age of 8 readmitted aged 16 dies aged 80

Elizabeth [4] admitted at the age of 10 dies after 83 years aged 93

More positive results of treatment

The tragic details of the exceptionally long stay patients, can be softened, by some other outcomes, that can perhaps be more positively interpreted as the 'happily ever afters'.

Females due to potential change of name in future marriages could not be as easily traced on Census search systems as males: –

Mary [2] an 'idiot' is 'discharged by her father's order' at the age of 8, to be back home with her father a timber dealer and her family. She only received treatment for 15 months. Her father James who died in April 1879 left very strict instructions in his last will and testament: –

'...in trust to pay and divide the same unto equally between my said three children Zillah W John W and Frances Sarah W. Subject nevertheless to their continuing to maintain clothe and provide for my said daughter Mary W during her life at their joint expense'. Mary eventually dies aged 23 in Billesdon.

Mary [3] Discharged home recovered on 11th July 1868. On the 1871 Census she is back with her parents in Paynes Yard working as a shoe fitter.

Mary Ann [1] an 'imbecile' is released 'relieved' in 1878 and returns home to her family an iron striker's house in Derby in March 1878.

Charles [2] who was admitted with dementia aged 14 is released in 1907. In 1911 he was living with his cousin and they are both gardeners, his father is still a blacksmith in Shepshed. He may not have been strong enough to learn his father's trade and his interest in gardening had been borne at the 1st County Asylum. .

Walter released in 1909 was back home with his family in 1911 with his brothers and sisters working as a shoe hand.

Edmund who was 'naturally deficient in intellect' was discharged recovered in 1884 – he is not found on the 1891 Census, but in 1901 there is a man of his age and county birth location working as a domestic groom as his father had been. He is married to Jane with 4 children.

William Christmas was in later years to live in London, where he died aged 78.

One of the most interesting of the young patients is Alfred [3]. Even though he remained a single man, his occupational pattern would have been mirrored by many other men of the same age, who had never needed treatment in a lunatic asylum:– Alfred [3] was born in Raunds Northamptonshire and admitted in 1876 aged 7 with epileptic mania. He was discharged recovered in 1877. In 1881 he is a scholar aged 12 with his parents in Gresham Street, Leicester. His father is a shoemaker. By 1891 aged 22 he is boarding as a shoe riveter in St Margarets, central Leicester. On the 1901 Census he is aged 32 and a boot maker boarder in Kettering. There were obviously better job prospects elsewhere as by 1911 he is in a boarding House at Llanhowell, Llanryan Pembrokeshire with an occupation recorded as a labourer in a stone quarry there.

Patients admitted from workhouses

One of the most interesting outcomes is that few, if hardly any of those who were admitted from Union Workhouse from all over Leicestershire, were ever relocated there. Maria [2] was the only young patient found to have been relocated to a Union Workhouse.

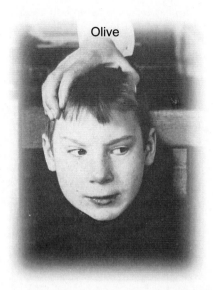

Olive

So many of them remained asylum patients. Maria[1] was obviously going to have to stay in 1851 as she had been 'under medical treatment and subjected to personal restraint'. The young well behaved like the foundling Emily [1] and those whose dire behaviours had been successfully modified, were not relocated back to their previous workhouse.

Was it to be generally believed that once they had the status of a patient needing treatment, they could no longer classified as a 'workhouse inmate? Was it also generally believed by those apportioning care, that life as an asylum patient had better future life patterns, than those in the Union, even though it was more expensive?

Modernisation and Change

Life was not standing still. The patients whatever their age, were working amongst constant modernisations. The introduction of telegrams enabled relatives to have more immediate contact with asylum patients and vice versa. There were also the new technological devices such as the skiagraphs (early X–Rays) and photographs.

> *'I think it desirable that the patients should be photographed on admission and discharge and I recommend that the necessary apparatus be purchased at a cost of from ten to twelve pounds'. January 2nd 1900 Borough Asylum*

Occupational experiences were often gained on new updated equipment or energy sources.

> *'The laundry extension is nearly completed and the question as to whether it should be lighted by electricity or gas should now be considered'. January 9th 1901*

The later case books with photographs from 1893 (1st County Asylum) really help to put us in the picture. With many of the later admissions, having a second photograph, which from their improved appearance, was assumedly taken, when the patient had recovered or was about to be released. The second photograph essentially functioned as a token of success, even though Charles[3] appears to be taking both photographic sessions extremely seriously.

Charles [3]

Charles [3]

Conclusion

Thousands of patients were admitted to the first two asylums in Leicestershire during the 19th and earliest years of the 20th centuries. At any one time, about less than one percent of the total of those receiving care, in any of the 3 asylums, were aged 14 and under. The young ones were very much minors and in the minority. They came through the Asylum doors, not to be locked away: They came to be treated. The following extract taken from the asylum regulations highlights how they could be expected to be cared for: -

> *'Confinement, probation or punishment of any inmate' was forbidden without medical authority. There was to be 'no deceit or terrifying of patients, or irritation by mockery or mimicry'. The keepers 'shall not indulge or express vindictive feelings'; they were to 'forgive all petulance on the part of the patients and treat with equal tenderness those who give the least trouble'.* [78]

It was imperative that the vast asylum complexes to which they where taken functioned as a 'home from home', even though the differences from the life experience of their own homesteads would probably have been phenomenal. Within the asylum family, a priceless endowment was given to many of the young ones. Many were acquiring life experiences and levels of care, that their peer groups in the outside world would not have been getting; they were able to experience a safe independence. It is very impressive that they were out and about with opportunities to be successfully industrious, regardless of any major negativity within their performance.

The opportunities were there for the youngsters to discover happiness in their own terms. For some it was discovered whilst being enlisted as a member of the asylum workforce. From Ruth[79] delighting in getting soaking wet whilst at work in the laundry, to Thomas3 skylarking with barrows whilst labouring on the farm and another Thomas[6] taking pleasure in his evening game of cricket, joy was readily available.

Those with permanent learning difficulties of any age were though essentially sadly inconvenient asylum admissions – taking up the much–needed places, which would have been readily filled by the more potentially curable. The numbers of these 'long term' patients are constantly frustratingly referred to when asylums were over full, with few or no free places.

However, in becoming exceptionally problematic patients to treat, they potentially gave the asylum members of staff a wealth of experience within their professional careers. Their behaviours continually posed questions, which were essentially quite complex to answer, if strict staff procedures were to be adhered to.

During the 18 and early 1900s, the most clearly defined condition for the younger patients was 'epileptic mania'. Schizophrenia itself as a mental condition, is barely a hundred years old. Within the case books, the only clear distinction between learning disabilities were the terms 'idiot' or 'imbecile'. In the later individual records, with photographic inclusions, only one image was noted of a patient suspected of having the genetic defect of Downs Syndrome[79]. The opening years of the 20th Century do in

---

78   Asylum Regulations 1837, Rules 1849 and 1894 Leicestershire's Lunatics – The Institutional care of Leicestershire's Lunatics during the Nineteenth Century H G Orme W H Brock Leicestershire Museums and Art Galleries 1987 ISBN 085022 227 3
79   1ˢᵗ County Asylum case book DE 3533-189-1998

many ways appear to take the form of the age of enlightenment. It would though be many more decades before any further congenital syndromes or conditions resulting in intellectual disability would be identified.

With these advancements in diagnosis and understanding, perhaps the most significant change to the care systems of many decades ago, was that the patients from 1912, were no longer being admitted to lunatic asylums. Young Lily and Beatrice both aged 9, George Henry aged 10 and the infant Joseph Montague aged just 4, were all part of a new age – for on their admissions in 1912, they were not new patients in a lunatic asylum, they were all photographed as incoming patients to a mental hospital.

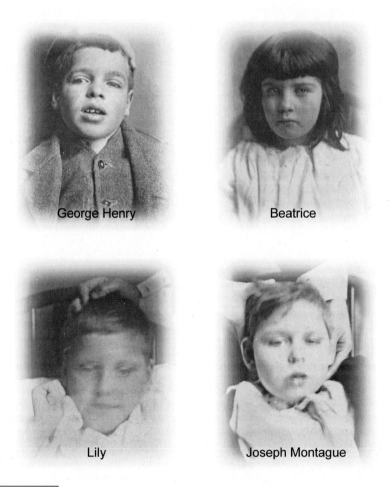

George Henry

Beatrice

Lily

Joseph Montague

---

79   Lillian Nellie (3533-214-29) was admitted in her twenties, she was recorded 'presents characteristics of Mongolian idiocy' In 1866 that the English physician John Langdon, Down noted the physical characteristics of those with Mongoloid features & published his findings.

A Lunatic Asylum

*Early drawing of the 1st County Asylum 1849 from an engraving by H Adland.
Courtesy of the University of Leicester Archives.*

A Mental Hospital

*2ⁿᵈ County Asylum Carlton Hayes) Main Entrance in later years – Photograph Courtesy of
Leicestershire, Leicester & Rutland Record Office*

Primary Sources

1st County Asylum Patient Case Books DE3533–

185–Nos 576–891	Jan 1845 to Aug 1848
186–Nos 892–1314	Aug 1848 to Dec 1852
187–Nos 1315–1733	Dec 1852 to June 1856
188–Nos 1734–1972	June 1856 to Sept 1858
189–Nos 1973–2269	Sept 1858 to May 1861
190–Nos 2270–2566	May 1861 to Jan 1865
191–Nos 2567–2838	Jan 1865 to March 1868
192–Nos 2839–3088	March 1868 to Jan 1870
193–Nos 3089–3395	Jan 1870 to Aug 1873
194–Nos 3396–3740	Aug 1873 to April 1877
195–Nos 3741–4105	April 1877 to Sept 1880
196–Nos 4106–4404	Sept 1880 to Aug 1883
197–Nos 4401–4799	Aug 1883 to Oct 1887 No.s 4401 to 4404 Used Twice
198–Nos 4800–5000	Oct 1887 to Oct 1889
199–Nos 5001–5201	Oct 1889 to Aug 1891
200–Nos 5202–5402	Aug 1891 to March 1893
201–Nos 5403–5603	March 1893 to April 1895 No.s 5604 to 5753 missing
202–Nos 5754–5903	July 1896 to Dec 1897 No.s 5904 to 6055 missing
203–Nos 6056–6205	April 1899 to Dec 1900

From this point patients identified by page number only.

204 Male patients only from	Dec 1900 to Aug 1903
205 Male patients only	Aug 1903 to Jan 1906
206 Male patients only	March 1906 to Sept 1908
207 Male patients only	Sept 1908 to Jan 1911
208 Male patients only	Jan 1911 to Jun 1913
210 Female patients only	Dec 1900 to Aug 1903
211 Female patients only	Aug 1903 to Feb 1906
212 Female patients only	Feb 1906 to July 1908
213 Female patients only	Aug 1908 to Oct 1908

(The case books continue from this date when the last patients had left but it is assumed that the case books continued to be used in the new asylum).

214 Female patients only	Nov 1910 to Oct 1913

Borough Asylum Case Books DE2853

177 Case Book E	May 1895 to Apr 1904
178 Case Book F	1898 to 1906
179 Case Book H Male	Sept 1902 to July 1912
180 Case Book J Female	May 1909 to Aug 1912
181 Case Book 26 Male and Female From	May 1899 to Mar 1900
182 Case Book 27 Male from	Jan 1900 to Apr 1901
183 Case Book 28 Female from	Apr 1900 to Mar 1901
184 Case Book 29 Female from	Mar 1901 to Jun 1901
185 Case Book 30 Male from	Apr 1901 o Apr 1902
186 Case Book 31 Female from	Jun 1901 to Oct 1901
187 Case Book 32 Female from	Oct 1901 to Nov 1902
188 Case Book 33 Male from	Apr 1902 to Aug 1903
189 Case Book 34 Female from	Nov 1902 to Apr 1903
190 Case Book 35 Male	Apr 1903 to Nov 1903
191 Case Book 36 Male from	Aug 1903 to Dec 1904
192 Case Book 37 Female from	Nov 1903 to Oct 1904
193 Case Book 38 Female from	Oct 1904 to Sept 1905
194 Case Book 40 Female from	Sept 1905 to Jul 1906
195 Case Book 41 Male from	Mar 1906 to Jun 1907
196 Case Book 42 Female from	Jul 1906 to Jun 1907
197 Case Book 43 Female from	Jun 1907 to Jul 1908
198 Case Book 44 Male from	Jul 1907 to Jan 1909
199 Case Book 45 Female from	Jul 1908 to Jun 1909
200 Case Book 46 Male from	Jan 1909 to Jul 1910
201 Case Book 47 Female from	Jun 1909 to Oct 1910
202 Case Book 48 Male from	Jul 1910 to Jan 1912
203 Case Book 49 Female from	Oct 1910 to Mar 1911
204 Case Book 50 Female from	Mar 1911 to Jan 1912
205 Case Book 51 Male from	Jan 1912 to Feb 1912

DE3533– Reception Order Certificate 1st and 2nd County Asylums

DE2853 Reception Order Certificates Borough Asylum

Salaries and Wages March 1849–Dec 1862 DE3533–94

1st County Asylum Medical Superintendent's Journal and Report Book DE3533–

83 from	Sept 1853 to Jan1862
84 from	Jan 1862 to Dec 1870
85 from	Jan 1871 to 1880
86 from	June 1880 to Sept 1884
87 from	Oct 1884 to Dec 1889
88 from	Jan 1890 to May 1894
89 from	June 1894 to June 1902
90 from	July 1902 to Nov 1910

Borough Asylum Medical Superintendent's Journals DE2853

Journal 1–40 from	Apr 1871 to June 1875
Journal 2–41 from	June 1875 to Nov1880
Journal 3–42 from	Nov 1880 to Dec 1888
Journal 4–43 from	Dec1888 to Dec 1897
Journal 5–44 from	Dec 1897 to Jun 1904
Journal 6–45 from	Jun 1904 to Jan 1912
Journal 7–46 from	Jan 1912 to May 1914

Borough Asylum Medical Superintendent's Diaries DE2853

65 from	Mar 1894 to Jun 1897
66 from	**Jun 1900 to Jan 1903**

Borough Staff Register DE2853–90 Dec 1903 to Apr 1910

DE3533/145 – 147 Registers of Admissions, Discharges, Transfers and Deaths with associated records May 1837 – March 1896

Borough Asylum Register of Patients DE2853

117	Sept 1869 to Aug 1892
119	Aug 1892 to Aug 1895
120	Sept 1895 to Jan 1901
121	Jan 1901 to Apr 1903
122	Apr 1903 to Aug 1906
123	Aug 1906 to Dec 1906

DE2853–89 Applications to work at Borough Asylum

DE2853–33 Special Account Cash Book Recording income from legacies and corporation loans and expenditure on sundries for patients.

DE3533 Charity Case Books –

217 – Nos 1 to 301	Nov 1839 to Sept 1888
218 – Nos 301 to 469	Sept 1888 to 1908

DE3533–9A Asylum House Visitors Book

DE3533 QS107/2/5 1st County Asylum Charity Ledger

DE3533–70 Financial Statements Book

DE3533/130B/1 County Asylum Matron Duties

DE3421–10 Lay out of 2nd County Asylum Buildings

DE3533–277/278 Leicestershire and Rutland Lunatic Asylum 1869 Annual Report

Leicestershire and Rutland County Medical Journals LRO Leicestershire and Rutland Lunatic Asylum. Rules for the General Management of the Institution with Prefactory Remarks by the Committee of Visitors I.S. Crossley Leicester 1849

DE3107–197 Sunneyholme Account Records– A home for feeble minded girls in 1924 where twelve yards of rubber sheeting is being purchased. It is not clear when this type of sheeting was first available for use in Leicestershire Asylums.

DE3421–10 Lay out of 2nd County Asylum Buildings

Secondary Sources

Leicestershire's Lunatics – The Institutional care of Leicestershire's Lunatics during the Nineteenth Century H G Orme W H Brock Leicestershire Museums and Art Galleries 1987 ISBN 085022 227 3

Committee of Visitors Prefatory Remarks Rules 1849 Leicestershire's Lunatics H Orme and W Brock Leics Museums and Art Galleries Record Service 1987 ISBN 085022 2273.

The History of Psychiatry Edward Shorter John Wiley and Sons 978-0-471-24531-5

Australian Geographic No 14 April–June 1989 Leech Mania Graeme Sims

Illustrations

An Etching by James Murray (the only patient whose full name is given) of the Leicestershire and Rutland Lunatic Asylum January 1890 Courtesy of University of Leicester Archives ULA/IMA2/2

Early drawing of the Asylum in 1849 by T Wilson is reproduced from an engraving by H Adlard to be used in Annual Reports Courtesy of the University of Leicester Archives

Drawings of Borough and 2nd County Asylum Tony Lockley

Plan of 2nd County Asylum Buildings Tony Lockley

Photograph of a stack of the Asylum Case Books taken at Leicestershire County Record Office. Tony Lockley

Photograph of an entry sheet within the case books taken at Leicestershire County Record Office. Tony Lockley

Photographs of Wards - Stewart Collection - Courtesy of the Record Office for Leicestershire, Leicester & Rutland, South Wigston

Photographs of Recreational Hall (opening day), an epileptic ward & the Main Entrance - 2nd County Asylum - Courtesy of the Record Office for Leicestershire, Leicester & Rutland, South Wigston DE3533/380B

Photographs of an Asylum Head Nurse - Stewart Collection - Courtesy of the Record Office for Leicestershire, Leicester & Rutland, South Wigston

Photograph of Dr Rothsay C. Stewart one of the former Medical Superintendents - Stewart Collection - Courtesy of the Record Office for Leicestershire, Leicester & Rutland, South Wigston

The north-east quadrangle of the Asylum, which would have been used as an airing court for female clients. 1920's photographs – Courtesy University of Leicester Archives

Aerial photograph of the Fielding Johnson Building taken during the early 1930's. FG1/3/96 Courtesy of University of Leicester Archives

Photograph of the Recreation Room Christmas 1890's Stewart Collection - Courtesy of the Record Office for Leicestershire, Leicester & Rutland, South Wigston

Photograph of front gardens 1st County Asylum - Courtesy of University of Leicester Archives ULA/FG1/3/10

Various individual photographs are taken from the later Case Notes Records of the 1st & 2nd Leicestershire and Rutland County Lunatic Asylums and the Borough Asylum. Specific individual images can be located by using patient reference numbers on the following pages. Courtesy of the Record Office for Leicestershire, Leicester & Rutland, South Wigston.

Patient Reference Numbers

Christian Names & Identification Number	Age	Asylum Reference Code	No in order of admission	Form of Mental Disord
Agnes	11	DE3533–197	4483	Learning Difficulty
Albert Isaac	13	DE3533–205	Page 126	Learning Difficulty
Albert–	9	DE2853–191–36	4885	Learning Difficulty
Alfred John	11	DE2853–120	3324	Learning Difficulty
Alfred[1]	13	DE3533–203	6164–205–Page 45	Learning Difficulty 2nd time Mental Illness
Alfred[2]	10	DE3533–206	Page 130	Learning Difficulty
Alfred[3]	7	DE2853–114–115	861	Mental Illness
Ann	13	DE3533–190	2547	Learning Difficulty
Annie	10	DE2853–120	3617	Learning Difficulty
Archibald	14	DE3533–202	5841	Learning Difficulty
Arthur[1]	14	DE3533–200	5237	Learning Difficulty
Arthur[2]	9	DE3533–200	5345	Learning Difficulty
Arthur[3]	12	DE2853–114–115	1397	Learning Difficulty
Arthur[4]	4	DE3533–195	3757	Learning Difficulty
Arthur[5]	10	DE2853–114–115	1540	Learning Difficulty
Arthur[6]	11	DE2853–200–46	5858	Mental Illness
Beatrice	9	DE3533–214	Page 133	Learning Difficulty
Bertie	13	DE3533–204	Page 92	Learning Difficulty
Betsy	11	DE3533–190	2517	Learning Difficulty
Cecil William	4	DE3533–204	Page 23	Learning Difficulty
Cecil	9	DE2853–120	3497	Learning Difficulty
Charles Percy	4	DE3533–207	Page 31	Learning Difficulty
Charles[1]	14	DE3533–201	5558	Learning Difficulty
Charles[2]	14	DE3533–206	Page 48	Mental Illness
Charles[3]	14	DE3533–207	Page 146	Mental Illness
Donald	9	DE2853–115–117	2228	Learning Difficulty
Duncan	6	DE2853–190	4747	Learning Difficulty
Edgar William	8	DE2853–191–36	4886	Learning Difficulty
Edith	5	DE3533–199	5027	Learning Difficulty
Edmund	14	DE3533–197	4458	Learning Difficulty
Edward	12	DE3533–190	2276	Learning Difficulty
Elizabeth Mary	11	DE3533–185	593	Learning Difficulty
Elizabeth[1]	12	DE3533–191	2771–3020	Learning Difficulty

Elizabeth[2]	8	DE3533–190	2347	Learning Difficulty
Elizabeth[3]	12	DE3533–202	5802	Learning Difficulty
Elizabeth[4]	10	DE3533–200	5224	Learning Difficulty
Elsie Matilda	9	DE3533–210	Page 104	Learning Difficulty
Elsie	10	DE3533–213	Page 11	Learning Difficulty
Emily[1]	10	DE3533–196	4265	Learning Difficulty
Emily[2]	12	DE3533–185	788	Learning Difficulty
Emma[1]	11	DE2853–119	3155	Learning Difficulty
Emma[2]	8	DE3533–186	978–1091	Mental Illness
Ethela Isola	7	DE3533–212	Page 61	Learning Difficulty
Eunice	12	DE2853–194–40	5269	Learning Difficulty
Florence Beatrice	11	DE2853–124	5879	Learning Difficulty
Frances Anne Elizabeth	14	DE3533–210	Page 88	Learning Difficulty
Fred	12	DE3533–199	5107	Learning Difficulty
Frederick[1]	13	DE3533–199–200	5145–5340	Mental Illness
Frederick[2]	6	DE2853–188	4618	Learning Difficulty
Frederick[3]	7	DE3533–193	3175	Learning Difficulty
George Henry	10	DE3533–208	Page 107	Learning Difficulty
George[1]	14	DE2853–117	777	Mental Illness
George[2]	14	DE3533–186	1028	Mental Illness
George[3]	12	DE3533–197	4748	Learning Difficulty
George[4]	12	DE3533–205	Page 2	Learning Difficulty
George[5]	13	DE3533–205	Page 94	Learning Difficulty
George[6]	14	DE3533–195	3929	Learning Difficulty
Gertrude	14	DE2853–121	4515	Mental Illness
Harriett	10	DE3533–190	2496–	Learning Difficulty
Henry Simon	6	DE2853–117	1667	Learning Difficulty
Henry[1]	14	DE3533–198	4901	Mental Illness
Henry[2]	14	DE3533–190	2544	Learning Difficulty
Henry[3]	8	DE3533–191	2588	Learning Difficulty
Henry[4]	13	DE2853–117	1410	Learning Difficulty
Herbert	7	DE2853–198	5682	Learning Difficulty
Hilda	11	DE3533–213	Page 136	Learning Difficulty
Horace	5	DE3533–203	6076	Learning Difficulty
Ida Elizabeth Mary	11	DE3533–199	5023	Learning Difficulty
Ida Winifred	12	DE3533–211	Page 71	Learning Difficulty
Isaac	12	DE2853–117	770	Learning Difficulty

James[1]	14	DE3533–190	2491	Learning Difficulty
James[2]	12	DE2853–124	5595	Learning Difficulty
James[3]	9	DE3533–194	3686	Learning Difficulty
Jane[1]	11	DE3533–197	4563	Learning Difficulty
Jane[2]	14	DE2853–119	3023	Mental Illness
Janet Winnie	5	DE2853–194–40	5232	Learning Difficulty
John Alpheus	8.5	DE3533–193	3342	Learning Difficulty
John Samuel Clifford	6	DE2853–191–36	4867–4982	Learning Difficulty
John William[1]	5	DE3533–196	4272	Learning Difficulty
John William[2]	6	DE3533–206	Page 10	Learning Difficulty
John William[3]	5	DE3533–195	3778	Learning Difficulty
John William[4]	12	DE3533–208	Page 24	Learning Difficulty
John[1]	13	DE3533–185	863	Learning Difficulty
John[2]	9	DE3533–193	3347	Learning Difficulty
Joseph Montague	4	DE3533–208	Page 108	Learning Difficulty
Joseph	3	DE3533–237	Adm Cert	Learning Difficulty
Lily	9	DE3533–214	Page 85	Learning Difficulty
Louisa	14	DE2853–117	1729	Mental Illness
Mabel Keziah	5	DE3533–210	Page 114	Learning Difficulty
Mabel	7	DE3533–210	Page 92	Learning Difficulty
Maria Martha	9	DE3533–196	4163	Learning Difficulty
Maria[1]	7	DE3533–185	818–1229	Learning Difficulty
Maria[2]	14	DE3533–186–187	1191–1379	Mental Illness
Mary Ann[1]	14	DE3533–197	4705–4767–5447–5599	Mental Illness
Mary Ann[2]	12	DE3533–191	2717–4169	Learning Difficulty
Mary Beryl	6	DE3533–214	Page 56	Learning Difficulty
Mary Elizabeth	14	DE3533–201	5552	Learning Difficulty
Mary Jane	13	DE3533–185	709	Mental Illness
Mary[1]	5	DE3533–196	4384	Learning Difficulty
Mary[2]	7	DE3533–192	2855	Learning Difficulty
Mary[3]	14	DE3533–191	2835	Mental Illness
Millicent	11	DE3533–189	2195	Learning Difficulty
Muriel Gertrude	10	DE3533–213	Page 9	Learning Difficulty
Naomi Millicent	11	DE3533–210	Page 107	Learning Difficulty
Olive	9	DE3533–213	145	Learning Difficulty
Reginald Thomas	6	DE2853–200–46	5843	Learning Difficulty

Reginald William	5	DE3533–207	Page 105	Learning Difficulty
Sarah Elizabeth	9	DE3533 –192 DE2853–173–23	3052	Learning Difficulty
Sarah Jane	14	DE3533–200	5210	Learning Difficulty
Sarah Susan Ravina	14	DE3533–213	Page 120	Learning Difficulty
Sarah	11	DE3533–190	2320	Learning Difficulty
Stanley William	11	DE3533–207	Page 74	Learning Difficulty
Thomas[1]	6	DE3533–206	Page 98	Learning Difficulty
Thomas[2]	8	DE3533–189	2203	Mental Illness
Thomas[3]	14	DE2853–117	737	Learning Difficulty
Thomas[4]	10	DE3533–195	4037	Learning Difficulty
Thomas[5]	13	DE3533–207	Page 73	Learning Difficulty
Thomas[6]	13	DE3533–197	4602	Mental Illness
Thomas[7]	14	DE2853–182	3885	Mental Illness
Thomas[8]	12	DE3533–190	2319–4049	Learning Difficulty
Violet Anne	8	DE2853–199–45	5772	Mental Illness
Walter James	7	DE3533–202	5878	Learning Difficulty
Walter	14	DE2853–124	5495	Mental Illness
William Christmas	14	DE2853–197–43 –DE3533–207	5641 Page 2	Mental Illness
William[1]	12	DE2853–117	1877	Learning Difficulty
William[2]	8	DE3533–196	4296	Learning Difficulty
William[3]	14	DE3533–195	4025	Learning Difficulty
William[4]	7	DE3533–190	2350–4050	Learning Difficulty
William[5]	13	DE3533–191	2724	Learning Difficulty
William[6]	10	DE3533–198	4882	Learning Difficulty
William[7]	14	DE3533–186	1132	Mental Illness
William[8]	14	DE3533–195	3852	Learning Difficulty
William[9]	11	DE3533–206	Page 90	Learning Difficulty
William[10]	10	DE2853–117	1771	Learning Difficulty
Willie	5	DE3533–199	5096	Learning Difficulty

The House of Cure

Life within the Leicestershire's 1st Lunatic Asylum
Taken from surviving historical records - Diane Lockley

The author's first book was the result of many years of research on medical records for the 1st County Lunatic Asylum (1837–1908), which was then sited at the University Of Leicester. These documents are still held at the Record Office of Leicestershire, Leicester and Rutland.

The intention of the publication was twofold. Firstly, to make other researchers or family descendants aware of the records existence: Secondly to instil a greater awareness of this asylum's continual forward thinking approaches to care and treatment, regardless of how treatable certain patients were.